TURNING UP
THE HEAT

OUR PERILOUS FUTURE
IN THE GLOBAL GREENHOUSE

By the same author:

WATERSHED:
THE WATER CRISIS IN BRITAIN, 1982
ACID RAIN, 1987

TURNING UP THE HEAT

OUR PERILOUS FUTURE
IN THE GLOBAL GREENHOUSE

FRED PEARCE

THE BODLEY HEAD
LONDON

A CIP catalogue record for this book is
available from the British Library

ISBN 0–370–31260–0

© Fred Pearce 1989

Printed and bound in
Great Britain for
The Bodley Head Ltd
31 Bedford Square
London WC1B 3SG
by Mackays of Chatham PLC
set in Times
by J&L Composition Ltd, Filey, North Yorkshire

First published 1989

CONTENTS

INTRODUCTION

THE SIGN

For those waiting for a sign, 1988 was the year they saw the greenhouse in action. If there was a moment that marked the sea-change in the view of scientists it came on 24 June 1988, at a hearing of the US Senate's Energy and Natural Resources Committee in Washington DC. 'It is time to stop waffling so much,' said Jim Hansen, the top climate investigator at NASA's Goddard Institute for Space Studies. 'We should say that the evidence is pretty strong that the greenhouse effect is here.'

He could not have chosen a better moment to speak up. That week, the US Agriculture Department had listed half the counties in the country, from Ohio to Montana and from Texas to North Dakota, as suffering from drought. The headlines said that half the grain crop was lost. Almost 2,000 barges sat useless on the Mississippi River. Water levels were ten metres below normal. There was too little water to keep the barges afloat on a river with the third largest drainage basin in the world. At Memphis, Tennessee, the river was at its lowest level since 1872. There were calls to drain the Great Lakes to keep the 'old man' rolling. Grizzled farm hands said there had been nothing like it since the 'dust bowl' years of 1934 and 1936. The story spread round the world in banner headlines. In London, the normally sober *Guardian* screamed on its front page the following morning: 'Pollution threat of scorched Earth'.

'It is not possible,' Hansen told the senators in a less well-publicized passage, 'to blame a specific heatwave or drought on the greenhouse effect.' But the American climate did appear to be doing what the mathematical models constructed at his laboratory predicted would happen in a greenhouse warming. And, hot from the computer printer, he had a readout of new data showing that the first five months of 1988 had set the world on target for the warmest year since records began 130 years before — warmer than 1987, the previous record-holder. The third, fourth and fifth warmest years had all been in the 1980s too. They were 1980, 1981 and 1983. 'We can state with about 99% certainty,' he told the committee, that 'current temperatures represent a real warming trend, rather than a chance fluctuation.' That did not prove it was the greenhouse effect, but did anybody have any better ideas?

Hansen got some flak from the science community for his outspokenness. Michael Schlesinger from the Climate Research Institute at Oregon State University, whose home state was then being hit by forest fires, said: 'If you look back to 1940, following the drought of the 1930s, people were making similar statements to what Jim is saying now, but we ended up having 35 years of cooling. We cannot afford to cry wolf again.' However, Hansen was talking about a global phenomenon, not a local aberration. And he was not the only climatologist with a very strong suspicion that this really was the long-awaited warming.

For two decades, the evidence had been accumulating that the release into the atmosphere of carbon dioxide, whether from the destruction of trees or the burning of fossil fuels, was bound to warm up the planet eventually. The gas holds the Sun's heat rather like the glass in a garden greenhouse. It lets in the Sun's rays, but traps the heat radiated back from the warmed ground. The concentration of carbon dioxide in the atmosphere had risen from some 270 parts per million (ppm) before the industrial revolution to around 350 ppm. There are other greenhouse gases released into the air by humans, notably methane, nitrous oxide and chlorofluorocarbons (CFCs), which have another life in the stratosphere, destroying ozone. Amounts of each of these gases in the atmosphere had also risen since the industrial revolution.

Introduction

But however hard the greenhouse watchers peered at their thermometers, none had been sure until 1988 that the planet was heating up as predicted.

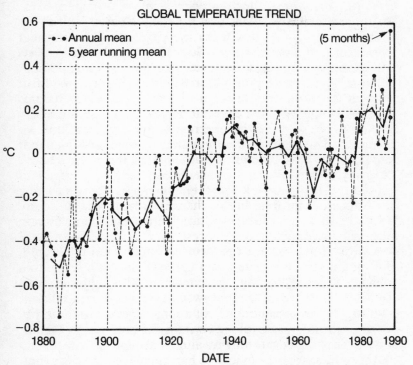

GLOBAL TEMPERATURE TREND

A century of global warming. The picture in mid-1988, when Hansen declared: 'The greenhouse effect is here.'

Richard Gammon of the US government's Pacific Marine Environmental Laboratory at Seattle in Washington state, seems to have been the first off the starting blocks. After seeing the complete data for 1987 and the first results from 1988, he told a conference in March 1988: 'Since the mid-1970s, we have been in a period of very, very rapid warming. We are ratcheting ourselves to a new warmer climate.' The world of the 1980s was turning out to be almost a degree centigrade warmer than the 1880s, and half a degree warmer than the average from 1950 to 1980. That may not

3

sound a lot, but only five degrees separate us from the depths of the last ice age.

The American claims about a global warming were confirmed by the world's leading analysts of past temperatures, Phil Jones and his team at the Climatic Research Unit of the University of East Anglia in England. Jones pointed out that in the southern hemisphere, seven of the eight hottest years in the past century had occurred between 1980 and 1987.

There is a great deal of natural variability in global temperatures from the ice ages, occurring once every 100,000 years, through the so-called 'little ice ages' arising every 2,000 years or so, to the essentially random events that make up much of our day-to-day weather. It is no accident that climatologists have pioneered mathematical theory on 'chaos'. They say that small random events can have very large and unpredictable outcomes. The flapping of a butterfly's wing in the Amazon rainforest could, theoretically, have caused the US drought. This makes spotting real trends and finding their causes very hard.

A whole range of short-term effects may upset the 'signal' of a greenhouse warming. Some effects, such as those from volcanoes, are reasonably well understood. Computers successfully predicted that 1982 would be cool after a massive eruption of the volcano El Chichon in Mexico blasted a veil of dust into the stratosphere in April of that year.

But the long-term warming in both the northern and southern hemispheres in the past century is at the very limit of anything known from the recent past. We are certainly moving beyond the still largely unexplained phenomenon of the little ice ages. These episodes of global cooling by about 1°C, lasting a few centuries, have occurred several times since the end of the last full ice age some 10,000 years ago. The most recent little ice age, during which the River Thames frequently froze in winter, began in medieval times and lasted until early in the nineteenth century. This variation is puny compared with what is coming. Hansen's computer predicts that within twenty years temperatures will be warmer than at any time for at least 200,000 years.

Introduction

The late 1980s are likely to be remembered for two things: the impact of Mikhail Gorbachev on the Soviet Union and world affairs ... and the sudden awareness of the need for global management of the life-support systems of our planet. We were softened up in 1983. That was the year when a mysterious sickness among trees spread across the northern hemisphere from Czechoslovakia to the Appalachians. It was the year when a major convulsion in the climate of the Pacific Ocean brought dust storms and forest fires to Australia and Indonesia, and torrential rains to normally arid Pacific islands and to the Americas. And it was the year when the world first heard of Wollo, Tigre and the other badlands of the Ethiopian famine. Nobody knew it at the time, but investigations into each phenomenon have since revealed that all three were linked.

Other developments in science gave a new understanding of how our planet works — and how its life-support systems might break down. The 1980s also saw a flurry of research into the wild climatic events that saw off the dinosaurs 65 million years ago. It seems that a direct hit by a meteorite started it all. And new theories about a 'nuclear winter' showed that blast and radioactive fallout were not the only things that would follow nuclear war. In climatic terms, a nuclear holocaust could be rather like the impact of a meteorite.

But it was the quite unexpected discovery in 1985 of a hole in the ozone shield above Antarctica which shocked the world into a new awareness about the predicament of our planet. It seemed that we could destroy life on our planet without even knowing what we were doing. The ozone hole had opened suddenly and without warning. It would probably continue to grow and there was little in the short term that we could do to stop it. The chemicals responsible had been let loose in the atmosphere decades before. As the scientists rapidly recalculated their models of the atmosphere to explain the hole, they began to wonder, along with the rest of us, what other surprises lay in store. Would the next one appear from the ocean depths, the ice sheets of Antarctica, or perhaps the Amazon rainforest?

5

New investigations of past climates offered no solace. There seemed to be no such thing as gradual change. A new climatological lexicon of 'lurches', 'flips' and 'triggers' emerged. And it seemed that tiny changes in heating, caused by wobbles in the Earth's orbit round the Sun, had triggered those lurches and flips — into and out of ice ages, for instance. As we turned up the heat, might we cause another climatic lurch?

A week after Hansen delivered his headline-grabbing warning on the greenhouse effect, the Canadian government hosted a major international meeting of researchers and policy-makers to discuss 'The Changing Atmosphere'. The conference was subtitled 'Implications for Global Security'. The scientists had no doubt about the gravity of the issues they were discussing.

Opening the conference, Kenneth Hare, the chairman of Canada's Climate Program Planning Board and a leading figure at the World Meteorological Organization, said: 'The human search for necessities such as warmth, industrial energy and food is altering the optical properties of the atmosphere, and thereby threatening world climate and the well-being of all living things.' He predicted 'a revolutionary change in world climate, of a sort not rivalled in the history of civilization, not since the abrupt end of glacial climates 10,000 years ago'.

The conference was an emotionally and intellectually charged affair. 'This conference is the Woodstock of the greenhouse effect,' declared Stephen Schneider, from the National Center for Atmospheric Research in Boulder, Colorado. He is one of the scientists from the Woodstock generation who seem destined to spend their lives charting the world's path into what some now call the greenhouse civilization.

The scientists felt that, with the world's attention on them, they had to bury their differences and uncertainties and put forward a common proposal to the world. Hare argued that their tentative predictions were at least as reliable as the prognostications of economists. 'If decision-makers are willing to listen to economists, they should be even readier to listen to us,' he said. Now the world was listening, they could not flunk their chance. In the end, the meeting called for a 50% cut in emissions of the main greenhouse gas, carbon dioxide, with a 20% cut in force by 2005. It also adopted a proposal from Michael McElroy, a red-headed Irishman from Harvard University, that nations should set up a world atmosphere fund to investigate both climatic change and the technologies that could halt it. The fund's coffers should be filled from a tax on the burning of fossil fuels by the industrialized nations. Making this happen 'would appear to require an international body with unprecedented power and autonomy,' said McElroy.

But there may be little choice ... We live in a world inextricably connected. The atmosphere is a global resource. National prerogatives and parochial interests must be subordinated to protect the rights of all the living elements of the planet. The question is, can we act in anticipation of the problem, or must we wait until the crisis is obvious, and the time for orderly process is past?

Small nations often lead the way in these matters. It was Sweden that organized a conference in 1972 which effectively launched the international environment movement. Now it was Canada's turn. The Prime Minister, Brian Mulroney, called for nations to work towards a Law of the Atmosphere, to complement the Law of the Sea and to be enacted in 1992. His call flew in the face of his more narrow-minded compatriots who predicted that Canada was well placed to benefit from a little global warming. It could bring to Canada the climate that makes the American midwestern grain fields the breadbasket of the world.

There were dissenters. John Maddox, editor of the top science journal *Nature*, wrote the following week, 'people who should know better have been talking as if they know the greenhouse effect has begun to work its way through our climate system.' He meant Hare and Hansen.

Taking a longer perspective, members of the Soviet Academy of Sciences wrote that month in the journal, *Science in the USSR*, that the greenhouse effect was to be encouraged. It could save the world from an ice age. 'Owing to cosmic factors,' they said, 'a million years from now the planet could become completely glaciated but for the active interference of man in nature.' They explained that 'coming changes in the planet's position in space, which will gradually build up over the next ten to fifteen thousand years, may cause a dramatic cooling of the climate ... An enhanced release of carbon dioxide as a result of human economic activity will likely delay the first glaciation by tens of thousands of years.'

AN OWN GOAL

Whatever future millenniums may bring, there is a growing certainty among climatologists that our planet is entering uncharted waters. As I hope to show in this book, pollution from greenhouse gases is only the start. By razing tropical rainforests we may be destroying nature's best defence against our depredations. Nature may respond by melting ice sheets and drowning cities, frazzling crops and leaving our reservoirs empty. The twenty years of drought and famine that have killed millions across the parched lands of Africa may be just the start. The strange sickness of forests which began in the early 1980s in Europe and North America could be a prelude to much worse to come.

The world's scientists are embarking on a major effort to understand the workings of our planet. It will be an endeavour as profound as the efforts of the past 50 years to understand the workings of our universe. The mind-blowing science of cosmology and particle physics may soon be supplanted in the public imagination by the hidden workings of the life-support systems of our planet. A sign of this change is the decision by space scientists to dedicate the International Space Year in 1992 to focusing on planet Earth. NASA has its separate and even more ambitious plan which it calls 'Earth Observing Systems' (EOS) or, more catchily, 'Mission to Planet Earth'.

The aim of all this science is, in essence, to write an operating manual for our planet. Clearly it must be an international task. Some groundwork was done when Ronald Reagan and Mikhail Gorbachev met in Washington DC in

Introduction

November 1987. They agreed 'to promote broad international and bilateral cooperation in the increasingly important area of global climate and environmental change'. Thomas Malone, one of the first American scientists to propose an international programme of research into the operation of the planet, wrote in a letter to the *New York Times* that the agreement was 'the best-kept secret of the Reagan–Gorbachev summit — and potentially the most portentous for global well-being during the twenty-first century'. At stake, he went on, 'is the continued robustness of the thin film of air, water, plants and soil through which biogeochemical cycling provides the life-support system to sustain an expanding world population'. One of the first fruits of the agreement was Soviet help with an American mission to probe the ozone layer over the Arctic the following winter.

The seeds of these efforts at collaboration go back three decades to 1957, International Geophysical Year. It was the first international effort at global science and has had profound implications for our thinking about our planet. The Year provided the impetus to set up, round the world, twenty or so ozone monitoring stations. Nearly three decades later, one of those stations, at Halley Bay in Antarctica, spotted the ozone hole. The Year also saw the start of a continuous measure of trace gases in the air on top of Mauna Loa in Hawaii, which first revealed the rise in global concentrations of carbon dioxide.

Global science has never looked back. Today, there is the World Ocean Circulation Experiment (WOCE), Tropical Ocean-Global Atmosphere (TOGA) and the Global Ocean Flux Study (GOFS), to name but three. For the 1990s, to oversee them all and fill in the gaps, comes the International Geosphere–Biosphere Project (IGBP). It is subtitled, more comprehensibly, 'A Study of Global Change'. The aim of the IGBP, which was inaugurated in 1986, is to answer 'what if' questions, such as 'what happens to the atmosphere if we chop down the Amazon rainforest?' or 'what if the loss of ozone in the stratosphere changes climate systems down below?' and 'what if global warming triggers sudden changes in ocean circulation?'

The man who chairs the committee set up to run the IGBP has, arguably, one of the most important and interesting jobs in the world. He is an American marine biologist, James McCarthy. When not investigating the future of the world, McCarthy runs a large collection of stuffed animals at the Museum of Comparative Zoology at Harvard University. The contrast between the ancient and modern worlds of biology could not be more stark. When I met him he had just finished showing a Soviet consul round a display of a butterfly collection assembled by Vladimir Nabokov, better known as the Russian author of *Lolita*.

'Our task,' he said, 'is to bring together all the research being done into global change.' His personal concern is how oceans and atmosphere interact. He believes one of the first effects of global warming could be to change the mixing processes in the surface layers of the oceans. It could speed up the melting of ice in Arctic waters. It could also upset the oceans' huge colonies of plankton, which control the amount of carbon dioxide that the oceans can absorb. If warming from the greenhouse effect cut down the oceans' ability to absorb carbon dioxide in this way, then the warming would accelerate. This 'positive feedback' could cause the process to spiral out of control.

One of the main tasks of the IGBP will be to try to identify these 'positive feedbacks'. It will also look at how global changes will affect individual countries. Some vulnerable environments are well known, such as the Sahel region of Africa. But what of the northern forests that cover Canada, Scandinavia and Siberia? Some ecologists say that in a warmer world the forests would flourish as never before. Others say they would wither and die. If they died, they would release large amounts of carbon dioxide into the air and warm our world even more. Who is right?

If global warming melts ice sheets, low-lying land will flood. In the Pacific, entire nations would disappear beneath the waves. Elsewhere, tides would wash hundreds of kilometres inland. Tens of millions of people live on the flood plain of the Yellow River in China. 'The river is already above the flood plain due to dyking. Fears of flooding are growing, especially if it comes suddenly,' says McCarthy.

Introduction

The river has killed before. During the Sino–Japanese War when the Kuomintang deliberately breached a dyke in 1938 to thwart a Japanese advance, they drowned an estimated 900,000 Chinese peasants — several times the toll of the atomic bomb that fell on Hiroshima seven years later. The breach remains the single most devastating act ever perpetrated by humans on their fellows, and it was an 'own goal'. But we could beat it soon enough.

SAVING OURSELVES

This book is about the perils that mankind and our planet run as we enter the greenhouse age. We visit the planetary 'hotspots', places where the future of the world may be spotted first: the Amazon rainforest and the droughtlands of the Sahara, the ozone layer over Antarctica and the icy seas around Iceland where water plunges to the ocean depths in a mysterious 1,000-year cycle. We ask how cars and cattle, termites and waste tips could influence our future. We explore the hidden links between apparently unrelated events during the 1980s — from red tides of algae and flooding in Bangladesh to African drought and the death of trees across Europe and North America — and talk to the scientists who say these events provide signposts to the far more disturbing events awaiting us in the coming century. We look for signs too in new discoveries about the causes of the ice ages and why life has flourished on Earth but not on our neighbours, Mars and Venus.

The book warns that the greenhouse age may turn out very different from that predicted by the climate modellers. Change may come suddenly, rather than slowly over decades. There may be entirely unexpected developments, such as the opening of the ozone hole. Most worrying of all, the greenhouse could trigger changes in the oceans or forests that escalate the greenhouse effect. But ultimately I am optimistic that we can, if we have a will, discover the basic laws that run the life-support systems of the Earth and organize ourselves to manage that system in a way that will save both ourselves and our planet.

1

THROUGH THE OZONE HOLE

The winter air high above the Antarctic is just about the coldest place on Earth. With the Sun out of sight for four months, the temperature of the air at around ten kilometres up, at the bottom of the stratosphere, plunges to below minus 90°C. The air forms a swirling vortex that sits high above the freezing continent. It is so cold that it can hold virtually no moisture. What moisture there is turns to tiny ice crystals which form an eerie blanket of translucent cloud. On the surfaces of those crystals a series of unique chemical reactions occur. The reactions were recorded for the first time in 1987, by equipment packed into an aircraft that flew through this 'polar vortex'. The reactions have, each spring since the mid-1970s, carved a hole in the ozone layer over Antarctica. And they are frightening the most sober scientists.

Ozone is a form of oxygen with molecules of three atoms, rather than the usual two. It is created by ultraviolet radiation from the Sun bombarding ordinary oxygen molecules, and forms a layer in the stratosphere between 10 and 50 kilometres above the Earth. Ozone is essential for life to survive on land or in the upper layers of the ocean. Until the ozone layer formed sometime within the past billion years, life on Earth had to skulk in the ocean depths. Paradoxically, while ozone is created by ultraviolet radiation, it serves us by protecting living organisms from the effect of that radiation. The reactions that have carved out the ozone hole threaten the very basis of life on Earth.

12

'It's a runaway effect,' says Joe Farman, a British atmospheric chemist. His painstaking analysis of ozone data collected at the Halley Bay Research Station in Antarctica first alerted the world to the hole. Jim Anderson from Harvard University, who designed instruments to measure the chemistry of the hole from aircraft, agrees. 'The Antarctic hole is so dramatic that even with my nose buried I am becoming increasingly concerned personally about it.'

What frightens the scientists most is that not one of them had predicted the opening of the hole, over Antarctica or anywhere else. Since the mid-1970s, some had suggested that chlorine emitted into the air from aerosol spray cans might cause a slow decline in the thickness of the ozone layer. It was something, they thought, that might concern humanity sometime in the middle of the twenty-first century. But Farman's data from Halley Bay brought consternation. They showed that, between 1975 and 1984, during the southern hemisphere's spring, the layer thinned to almost half its former size.

By 1987, things were yet worse. 'In one layer of the atmosphere eight kilometres thick, we actually lost 95% of the ozone in six weeks,' said Farman. Moreover, the hole extended out over the Southern Ocean, nudging the Falkland Islands and Australia, and lasting into early December. There was growing evidence that the ozone layer right round the world was thinning perceptibly, bringing fears of more skin cancers among humans, damage to crops and fisheries and drastic changes to climate. The world, as seen through the ozone hole, began to seem a more dangerous and unpredictable place.

The discovery of the ozone hole may have been sprung on the world with the publication of Farman's data in May 1985. But Farman had been contemplating the truth for some time. The equipment with which he had been measuring the ozone in the air above Halley Bay had been taking regular readings since 1957. The British Antarctic Survey, for which Farman works, had set up the monitor as part of Britain's contribution to the International Geophysical Year.

Ozone levels had waxed and waned with changing sunspot activity and routine climatic oscillations, but Farman and his colleagues saw no hint of drama until the early 1980s. Then a dip on the ozone graph, which had begun in the mid-1970s, began to look something more than routine. 'In 1982,' says Farman, 'we noticed strange depletions ... however ozone levels are notorious for bouncing about and our instruments were then rather old. The Americans with their satellite viewing of the Antarctic continent from 800 kilometres up had not spotted anything, so we decided to check the figures with newer instruments.'

He dispatched equipment from the Survey's headquarters outside Cambridge in England. The equipment produced the same startling results, with ozone levels plunging in August and September 1984. 'By October 1984, we were sure something dramatic was happening,' says Farman. His letter describing his findings and offering a first tentative explanation arrived at the London office of *Nature*, the top science journal, on Christmas Eve 1984. It then spent three months with reviewers, who assess the quality of the science, and two more months with sub-editors before finally appearing on 16 May 1985.

The lack of urgency in *Nature*'s offices did not infect the outside community of atmospheric chemists. They were appalled and acutely embarrassed. None of their computer models of the chemistry of the ozone layer had predicted the hole. Not only that, it swiftly transpired that they had been analysing their data on ozone in such a way that signs of a hole would not show up. The scientists at NASA had programmed the computers which collated the measurements made by an American satellite, Nimbus 7, to throw out any data showing levels of ozone more than a third less than the average. They thought any such 'anomalous' data was bound to be wrong, because it did not fit their models of what should be happening. When they re-analysed the raw data sent by the satellite to the computer, they discovered that it had all along been recording the hole.

The incident was a graphic example of scientists being seduced by their theoretical models and forgetting to keep an eye on the real world. As Farman put it in the introduction to his 1985 paper: 'Results from such models are often accepted by default. The inadequacy of this approach

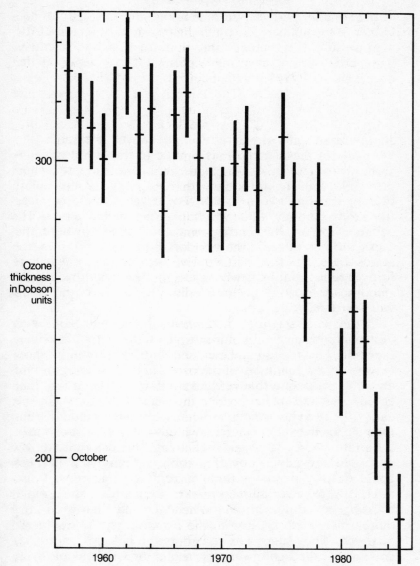

Formation of the ozone hole. Data on the thickness of the ozone layer over Halley Bay in Antarctica each October, as plotted by Farman and published in 1985.

is here made evident.' Bob Watson, the manager of the Upper Atmosphere Research Programme at NASA, the organization that goofed, put it more briskly: 'Scientists had become complacent. We thought we understood the processes.'

PLUGHOLE OF THE PLANET

Joe Farman calls the stratosphere above Antarctica the 'plughole of the planet'. This is close to the literal truth — certainly for ozone. As we have seen, ozone is created when ultraviolet light from the Sun breaks up oxygen molecules, thereby creating two free atoms of oxygen. Some of these free atoms combine with surviving oxygen molecules to form ozone. Most of this occurs over the equator, where the Sun's ultraviolet radiation penetrates most deeply into the atmosphere. But the circulation of the atmosphere, which is forever redistributing heat away from the tropics, eventually smoothes the ozone out into a layer that covers the globe like a protective sheath.

In the past, scientists had assumed that old ozone was destroyed primarily by further reactions with ultraviolet radiation. Destruction and creation of ozone were in balance. Now we know that in the modern world there is another fate awaiting the ozone that reaches Antarctica. It is a fate that could upset the ozone layer right round the planet. In the early 1970s scientists first warned that humans could disrupt the balance between the creation and destruction of ozone in the stratosphere. They said that nitrogen oxides emitted by a proposed new generation of supersonic high-flying airliners could destroy ozone. Except for a few Concordes, those aircraft were never built. But soon afterwards came a more pressing concern from Mario Molina and Sherwood (or, more usually, Sherry) Rowland of the University of California at Irvine. They suggested in 1974 that a group of industrial chemicals called chlorofluorocarbons, or CFCs, could waft up into the stratosphere and destroy ozone.

CFCs do not occur naturally. They were invented in 1930 by Thomas Midgley, who had fourteen years earlier invented another environmental timebomb — leaded petrol.

16

His employer, General Motors Frigidaire, asked him to find a coolant for refrigerators that was safer than ammonia, which they used at the time. Within two days, Midgley came up with CFCs and, in a famous demonstration, proved that the gas was neither toxic nor flammable by inhaling CFCs and blowing out a candle. After that, chemical companies used CFCs, which were very cheap to produce, for a wide range of purposes. The chemicals found jobs as cooling fluid inside the pipes of refrigerators and in air conditioning systems; as propellant in aerosol cans; and to make the bubbles in many plastic foams, such as those in egg boxes, soft furnishings and the packs that keep hamburgers warm at fast food restaurants.

Because CFCs are extremely stable, most decay only very slowly, and this is where their danger lies. While most CFCs begin life inside pipes, foams or cans, all are eventually released into the air as refrigerators leak, foam is crushed and aerosol cans empty. After that, they stay intact for many decades, gradually rising through the air until they reach the stratosphere. There, the intense ultraviolet radiation breaks them down, releasing chlorine atoms. This is where the action begins. The chlorine atoms strip one of the oxygen atoms from an ozone molecule to create a new chemical called chlorine monoxide, plus a molecule of oxygen. A second reaction may then follow in which chlorine monoxide reacts with free oxygen atoms to form ordinary oxygen molecules. Devastatingly, this leaves the chlorine atom free once more, to destroy more ozone. Given time and the opportunity, a single atom of chlorine can do immense damage to the ozone layer. Luckily, chlorine monoxide does not usually hang around in the atmosphere long enough to destroy too much ozone.

All this was outlined by Rowland and Molina in 1974. Through the mid-1970s, the threat that aerosol cans posed to the ozone layer won a lot of public attention. As Molina and Rowland had pointed out, CFCs 'are being added to the environment in steadily increasing amounts. They ... may remain in the atmosphere for 40 to 150 years, and concentrations can be expected to reach 10 to 130 times present levels.' With this in mind, the US and several Scandinavian countries banned CFCs in aerosol sprays during the late 1970s.

But the panic passed. The main makers of CFCs, such as DuPont in the US and ICI in Britain, said the case against their products was inconclusive. Atmospheric modellers predicted a slow thinning of the ozone layer. But nobody, least of all NASA's analysts of satellite data, could spot any actual decline in ozone in the stratosphere. Many scientists wrote it all off as another environmental scare. Rowland's colleagues remember that he took a lot of criticism for sticking to his warnings. All that changed with Farman's discovery of the Antarctic hole.

THE SMOKING GUN

In August 1987 some 160 scientists and technicians descended on Punta Arenas in Chile, the southernmost city in the world. Accommodation was somewhat cramped. There were only 108 hotel rooms in the town. The invaders, perhaps the most notable visitors since Ferdinand Magellan passed that way when finding a new route to the Pacific in 1520, were all there to help with flights into the ozone hole. The plane NASA chose for the job was an old U2 spy plane, the kind made famous in May 1959, when Gary Powers was shot down and captured over the Soviet Union. Now renamed the ER2 (for Earth Resources 2), the plane went on its first mission into the ozone hole on 17 August 1987, and repeated the journey eleven times before the beginning of October.

Expectations were high. 'I believe this is probably the single most important Earth science project in a decade,' said NASA's Bob Watson. One of the great disappointments for the scientists investigating the hole was that they could not personally fly with the ER2 through the stratospheric clouds which had upset their calculations. But the pilots who made the trips, such as Ron Williams who was later interviewed by *Time* magazine, spoke of flying into a continuous layer of translucent mist, quite unlike the broad clear skies they normally encounter on flights into the stratosphere. 'I went into cloud at 61,000 feet and I didn't come out the whole time,' said Williams.

The investigation was of the utmost urgency. There would be no leisurely trip back to their laboratories in North America and Europe before the scientists began to analyse the results. Still less would there be a long delay at the office of *Nature* before the public could hear about the findings. The scientists stayed put in Punta Arenas in a kind of brains trust to thrash out their conclusions, before flying back to Washington to present them in front of television cameras.

Before the expedition, there were two main theories about why the ozone hole formed. One said that, in the odd world of the polar vortex, some vast upwelling of air from the ground was bringing air free of ozone into the stratosphere. That would have been good news. No nasty chemistry was going on; it was all a freak of the local atmospheric circulation. The second view was that chemistry was to blame, that something new was happening, something dangerous. By the time the scientists returned to their press conference in Washington in the first week of October, the chemical theory had won.

There were fourteen separate instruments packed into the ER2 for its lonely 5,000-kilometre flights into the ozone hole. Nothing about the chemistry of the heart of the hole recorded by those instruments suggested an upwelling of air from below. The proponents of the chemical theory, who based their ideas on the work of Rowland and Molina, had predicted that the instruments would detect large amounts of chlorine monoxide. They called chlorine monoxide the 'smoking gun' that would show they were right. And the measurements from the flights found chlorine monoxide, masses of it. Concentrations ranged from 100 to 500 times the levels at similar altitudes elsewhere in the world. Moreover, the graphs drawn of the sudden surge in chlorine monoxide as the plane flew into the polar vortex, and the subsequent fluctuations within the vortex, were an exact mirror image of the ozone levels measured on the same flight. 'Ozone dropped precisely within the region defined by high chlorine monoxide,' said Anderson. As another scientist put it later, 'this was not so much a smoking gun as a signed confession'.

Chlorine, then, was the culprit. But how did it destroy ozone so much more efficiently than anyone had believed possible? The details of the process remained unclear. But, as Watson told the Washington press conference, the key seemed to lie in the ice crystals that make up the stratospheric cloud over Antarctica. Chemicals containing chlorine, notably CFCs, appeared to stick to the surfaces of the ice crystals in the stratospheric cloud and to release the chlorine atoms which destroy ozone. All the computer models had been based on chemical reactions between gases. Nobody had researched the role of solids, such as the ice crystals.

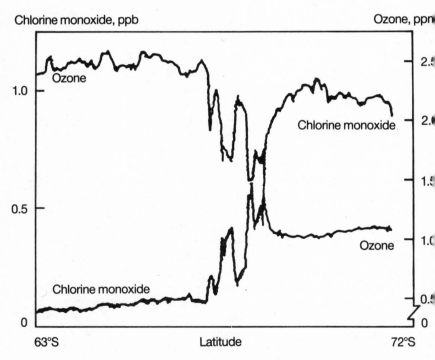

The 'smoking gun'. As the American research plane flew into the ozone hole, levels of chlorine monoxide rose as an exact mirror image of the fall in ozone levels. This, say the researchers, proves that chlorine does the damage.

That reflected a lack of curiosity among the scientists. Molina's and Rowland's original paper in 1974 warned that 'our calculations have been based entirely on reactions in the gas phase and essentially nothing is known of possible . . . reactions of chlorine atoms with particulate matter in the stratosphere.' Well, now we know about one such reaction.

Several factors have conspired together to produce the dramatic losses of ozone over the Antarctic each spring. One may have been revealed by the discovery that inside the polar vortex there is a sudden and almost complete disappearance of nitrogen oxides. These chemicals are found widely in the atmosphere and react with many other chemicals, not least chlorine monoxide, the critical chemical in the destruction of ozone. Normally, nitrogen oxides will react with any chlorine monoxide in the air, converting it swiftly to the less dangerous chlorine nitrate. They thus put a brake on the runaway destruction of ozone. Watson suggested that the ice crystals in the stratospheric cloud might be sabotaging the brake by collecting up the nitrogen oxides to form frozen dilute nitric acid. Such a process would leave the chlorine monoxide free to do its worst.

A second factor is the unique coldness of the stratosphere over Antarctica. The absence of sunlight during the Antarctic winter is the most obvious reason for this extreme cold. The other reason is the formation of the tight polar vortex of air which circulates in the stratosphere over the entire Antarctic land mass during winter. Anderson from Harvard describes it as being 'like a chemical containment vessel'. While it lasts, virtually nothing can get into or out of it. It might as well have brick walls. Without any warmer air breaking into the vortex, temperatures fall the critical extra two or three degrees thus allowing the stratospheric ice clouds to form. With no new air breaking into the vortex, the chlorine atoms, endlessly destroying ozone and freeing themselves to destroy more, have time to eliminate large amounts of ozone, so creating the 'hole'.

The ER2 flights found that inside the chemical containment vessel, ozone is destroyed at a rate of up to 2% per day. But this happens only when the final piece of the jigsaw

21

falls into place: the return of the Sun. During the Antarctic winter, chlorine monoxide accumulates in the vortex. The return of the Sun provides the ultraviolet light which releases the chlorine to destroy the ozone.

The ozone hole of 1987 was the deepest and longest lasting ever recorded. On average, half the ozone in the polar vortex was destroyed. In some places virtually all of it was obliterated. But why did the spring hole appear so suddenly in the late 1970s and deepen so much during the 1980s? It seems that the chlorine from CFCs accumulated in the atmosphere until some critical concentration was reached, beyond which the runaway reactions took off. Some investigators say that the balance between the nitrogen and chlorine compounds in the polar air was critical. When nitrogen dominated, it could destroy the chlorine before the chlorine did serious damage to the ozone. Once chlorine gained the upper hand, there was no stopping it.

Whatever the truth, it is clear that scientists did not predict the consequences. My colleague John Gribbin, author of a book on the ozone saga called *The Hole In The Sky*, puts it like this:

Imagine a naïve scientist watching a block of ice being heated slowly. As the temperature approached melting point he could still write in his notebook that, on the basis of what he had seen so far, he predicts no significant change in the ice block if it warms further. His prediction will be in ruins as soon as the block warms above 0°C.

THE SPREADING VORTEX

What happens next? With their statistical models still in tatters, ozone scientists spent the mid-1980s in a quandary. Some argued that the climate above Antarctica was so special that the ozone hole was a local phenomenon unlikely to be repeated. But the difficulty was not local. In March 1988, Watson was in front of television cameras again to reveal that the ozone hole was having an effect on parts of the southern hemisphere occupied by more than penguins and scientists. Severe falls in ozone levels were now, he said, 'a year-round phenomenon as far north as 60°S. And that is being conservative. Many people looking at the data would say it spreads to 40 to 45°S.' That takes in Tasmania.

The fall in ozone concentrations across the great Southern Ocean surrounding Antarctica may well be largely a result of the breakup of the polar vortex each summer. Ozone-depleted air spreads out and away from Antarctica, diluting the ozone layer over large parts of the southern hemisphere. But the worry is that the destruction of ozone may itself be intensifying the polar vortex, making it bigger and longer lasting. And that in turn would improve conditions for ozone destruction.

After the scientists headed back to Washington in October 1987, the hole persisted for more than a month longer than it had in 1985 or 1986. Temperatures in mid-October were around 5°C lower than normal. The vortex finally broke up in early December. By that time, it had broken anchor, drifting away from the Antarctic continent and out over the sea towards South Africa and Australia. Roger Atkinson of the Australian Bureau of Meteorology reported that Australian ozone monitoring stations saw a sharp drop in ozone levels in December 1987 as the polar vortex broke up. Over Melbourne, the drop lasted for three weeks.

An ozone hole which lasts into the summer is much more dangerous than one which peters out in late spring, says Watson. The ozone protects us from ultraviolet light. The light of a polar spring is weak, but by December, the height of the southern hemisphere's summer, it has power and the amount of radiation which can reach the ground through a hole in the ozone layer is much greater.

Currently, the hole has to form again from scratch each spring. Before the Sun rises in August, ozone levels have, up to now, remained much the same as for the past 30 years. But what if one year's hole could begin to make the next year's hole deeper? The late breakup of the polar vortex over Antarctica 'could be the first indication of major climatic change' resulting from the ozone hole, says Sherry Rowland. Since ozone absorbs heat, its presence helps warm the stratosphere. Its absence cools it. The longer the ozone hole lasts, the longer it will take the southern stratosphere to warm each summer. If the cooling persists too long, it could have a year-round effect, intensifying the cold in the next winter. That could cause a bigger vortex, more stratospheric cloud and a yet deeper and wider ozone hole.

Atmospheric chemists are finding it hard even to guess at the kinds of effects that loss of ozone in the stratosphere could have on our weather at ground level. A worrying aspect is that the greenhouse effect and ozone loss, although apparently unconnected, seem to reinforce each other. As carbon dioxide and other greenhouse gases trap more of the Sun's heat close to the ground, less reflected heat reaches the stratosphere, which cools. Similarly, loss of ozone both cools the stratosphere and lets more ultraviolet radiation penetrate to the ground. While the loss of ozone is not a prime cause of global warming, it does have a small warming effect.

Rowland says that temperatures at the top of the stratosphere could fall by as much as 30°C by the middle of the next century from the combined effects of ozone loss and the greenhouse effect. Rowland and others believe this change to the vertical temperature profile of the atmosphere could change weather patterns — perhaps by upsetting the fast, high, westerly winds, known as jet streams, which dictate weather in much of Europe, North America and Australia.

In colder air the Sun's radiation destroys less ozone. This means that above tropical regions the greenhouse effect could, by cooling the stratosphere, help to heal the ozone layer. But elsewhere, and especially in the Antarctic, the cold triggers ozone destruction by forming stratospheric clouds. One suggestion is that the greenhouse effect could itself have cooled the air above Antarctica to the slightly colder temperatures which have triggered the formation of the ozone hole. What is certain is that the interplay between these two fundamental changes to our atmosphere has great potential to produce surprising and alarming results.

SHRINKING FROM ULTRAVIOLET

As the research planes flew over Antarctica, the threat to the ozone layer forced its way back on to the front pages and into the in-trays of ministers for the first time in a decade. NASA, with its big budgets for research hardware, coordinated the science, while the Nairobi-based United Nations Environment Programme — one of the quieter backwaters of the UN — took the initiative in galvanizing governments to take action.

The public's immediate fear about the loss of the ozone layer was that it would cause a plague of skin cancers. Australians felt most at risk. The country already had the highest rate of skin cancer in the world, because its population of fair-skinned Anglo-Saxons insist on wearing next to no clothes in summer, and shirk the practice of having a siesta. As the ozone hole crept north from the Antarctic, there must have been a *frisson* of worry among any scientifically literate hotel owners on Bondi beach.

Among the richer people in many Western countries, skin cancer is the only type of cancer that is becoming increasingly common — apparently as a result of more time spent lazing near-naked on hot beaches. In the US, between a third and a half of all cancers are skin cancers. One study found three times more cases in sunny Texas than in snowy Iowa. Some types, notably melanoma, are extremely dangerous. Each year about 10,000 people round the world die of the disease.

A small thinning of the ozone layer will have a large impact on the rate of skin cancers. A 1% decrease in ozone in the stratosphere produces a 2% increase in ultraviolet radiation reaching the ground. Among white-skinned people, such a rise will produce an increase of 8% in rates of skin cancer. The Environmental Protection Agency in the US said in 1987 that a 1% reduction in the ozone layer would produce some 6,000 more skin cancers a year in the US. That sounds alarming, though the extra risk to an individual living in, say, Boston is only about the same as from moving south a little — to Washington DC. I doubt if Michael Dukakis worried much about this before running for president in 1988.

The Reagan administration, despite a presidential problem with cancer cells on the nose, sought to undermine the warnings from its Environmental Protection Agency. The interior secretary Donald Hodel proposed a bizarre extension of the administration's support for personal rather than communal solutions to problems. He advocated 'personal protection' against ultraviolet radiation. Government officials were reported to be considering a public campaign to persuade people to wear sunglasses and hats and to apply more suntan lotion as a means to meet the 'UV threat'. Meanwhile, one Australian scientist called for hats to be included in school uniforms and for trees to be planted in school playgrounds.

Ultraviolet radiation at dangerous wavelengths damages both proteins and DNA, the material that carries genetic information in living organisms. The radiation may either kill cells outright or cause cancers. It contributes in humans to sunburn, snow blindness and the ageing and wrinkling of skin. But the extent of the hazards range far beyond human skin. Many plants are vulnerable. According to the UNEP, sensitive crops include cotton, peas, soya beans, cabbages and many species of trees and grasses. Trials show that 'a 25% depletion of ozone levels would produce a 20 to 25% drop in soya bean yields'. Some pollens fail to germinate if there is too much ultraviolet light around. It is not clear whether smaller changes in exposure alter yields of crops.

The effects could be still worse in the sea. This is of immediate significance since the Antarctic ozone hole now spreads out into the Southern Ocean, which is one of the last great fishing areas of the world. Ultraviolet light can penetrate deep into clear sea water and, says the UNEP, poses a particular threat to algae. 'These are right at the bottom of the aquatic food chain, and if increased levels of UV led to severe damage ... the effect would be felt throughout aquatic ecosystems, perhaps leading to a decline in populations of edible fish.'

Sayed El-Sayed at the Texas A&M University believes he has already found evidence that algae in the seas around Antarctica are very sensitive to ultraviolet radiation. During a joint US–Polish trip to Antarctica in early 1987, El-Sayed's researchers found that after three days' exposure to natural ultraviolet light, algae grew at only a quarter of the rate of similar algae kept shaded from the radiation.

Daneb Karentz from the University of California at San Francisco spent early 1988 at the US's Palmer Research Station in Antarctica looking at the ability of organisms to repair damage done to their genes by ultraviolet light. Unless the damage is repaired, 'mutations affecting the physiology of the species and the genetic makeup of future generations can occur,' she said.

Extra UV light might also damage the larvae of individual species of fish. According to the UNEP 'recent research shows that all anchovy larvae can be killed up to a depth of ten metres by fifteen days' exposure to UV light some 20% higher than current levels.' Many would agree with Robin Russell Jones, a London specialist in skin diseases and a consultant to Friends of the Earth. He wrote in a medical journal in 1987 that, while millions of additional skin cancers could follow from likely reductions in the ozone layer, 'the effect on the aquatic food chain, fish production, and oxygen output from the ocean could dwarf the risks to human health.'

TIDY GRAPHS IN MONTREAL

Just as the ozone hole is a landmark in man's impact on the atmosphere, so the Montreal Protocol was a landmark in the response of mankind to global perils. Sixty-two governments, including those of all the major industrial nations, sat down in Montreal in September 1987 to thrash out the details of the protocol, which committed them to halving their output of the dangerous CFCs, primarily CFC-11 and CFC-12, by the end of the century.

As they took their seats, they knew that dozens of scientists were about to return from Punta Arenas with the most damning evidence yet that those chemicals were to blame for the destruction of ozone in the stratosphere. Even so, and despite the fact that negotiations had been going on all year, the fear persisted that no deal would be struck. The Americans feared that if they agreed to a cut other countries would step up production of CFCs. Richard Benedick, a senior American negotiator, had earlier accused Britain and its CFC manufacturer ICI of being 'more interested in short-term profits than in the protection of the environment for future generations'. His team suddenly proposed that the deal should not come into force until nations responsible for at least 90% of world production had signed. (They eventually settled for two-thirds.) The Russians demanded and got a special dispensation to allow them to complete two more CFC plants written into their current Five-Year Plan. The Europeans sat quiet. They already had the advantage, since most of their 50% cut in production could be made by removing CFCs from aerosol cans. The Americans, who had banned CFCs from aerosols years before, would have to end other uses.

Behind the national teams of diplomats were the big makers of CFCs, principally DuPont from the US and ICI from Britain. There was much gossip that DuPont was happy enough with tough new rules since it had got further than its rivals in developing substitute products. ICI had earlier that year helped to write a report for the British government which found that CFCs were 'unlikely to lead to a reduction of the stratospheric ozone layer'. Six months later, in March 1988, DuPont set the pace among manufacturers by announcing that it planned to phase out all use of dangerous CFCs, though it did not say by when.

As a sideshow, the Americans wanted to include halons in the protocol. Britain, for one, did not. Halons are compounds containing bromine, which is chemically similar to chlorine. Current estimates are that 40 times more CFCs are released into the atmosphere than halons. But halons are, according to conventional models, up to eight times more efficient than CFCs at destroying ozone. And there is a large reservoir of man-made bromine compounds locked up inside the world's fire extinguishers.

The meeting agreed that by 1992 production of halons should be restricted to less than the output in 1986. But the meat of the negotiations concerned CFCs, whose production was to be fixed in 1990 at the output of 1986, then cut back by 20% by 1995, and to 50% of the 1986 level by 1999.

The UNEP's director-general, Mostafa Tolba, hailed the agreement as a triumph, 'the first truly global treaty that offers protection to every single human being on this planet

. . . it seeks to anticipate and manage a world problem before it becomes an irreversible crisis.' Tolba's staff meteorologist predicted that it should keep ozone levels in the stratosphere to within 2% of their current level. That prediction was for many scientists palpable nonsense. It ignored the discoveries about the ozone hole. And it set aside new worries about ozone trends away from Antarctica. Those concerns were brought home just six months later, in March 1988, at yet another press conference at NASA's headquarters in Washington DC.

Once again, the television cameras were there in force. And once again, NASA's 'Mr Ozone', the bearded former Briton, Bob Watson, was in charge. Beside him was Sherry Rowland — the man who foretold it all, or almost all. This time it was not the Antarctic that grabbed the headlines, it was the Arctic. And the warnings were for Europeans and North Americans, rather than the citizens of Punta Arenas or Hobart.

For a couple of years, since Farman turned the ozone world upside-down, there had been rumours of a general thinning of the ozone layer right round the globe. But the evidence was uncertain. It came from two instruments aboard an American satellite, the Nimbus 7, which had been in orbit since 1978. The raw data from the satellite suggested that the ozone was disappearing at a rate of 1% a year, and 3% at certain latitudes. Nobody believed those figures. The consensus was that a mechanical diffuser plate which serviced both instruments had deteriorated producing spurious readings. But nobody knew how spurious.

In late 1986, Watson, prompted by publication of some dire predictions by his NASA colleague Donald Heath, set up an international team of scientists to investigate. Known as the 'Ozone Trends Panel', its task was to reassess the masses of data from ground monitoring stations operating instruments similar to the one at Halley Bay which had spotted the ozone hole. In March 1988, Watson presented the findings of the panel. The conclusions did not bear out Heath's interpretations of the satellite data. But they did provide evidence that there was a dent, if not a hole, in the ozone layer above the Arctic in December, January and

February. The absence of a tight polar vortex in the strato-sphere above the Arctic in winter moderated the local effects, but also tended to spread them.

At latitudes between 53°N and 64°N, there had been a reduction of around 6% in ozone every winter since 1969. Each January the fall approached 9%. These latitudes include most of Canada, all of Scandinavia and the Soviet Baltic, as well as Britain as far south as Nottingham. Further south, in a band stretching to 40°N and including all of Europe and the north-eastern states of the US, the winter loss was scarcely less at 4.7%. For sunbathers, the more important news was the levels in summer. This is the time when the Sun's radiation bombards the Earth most intensely, making any loss of ozone more critical. It is also, of course, when sunbathers take off their clothes. From Blackpool to Ibiza and Long Island to the Black Sea, there was in 1986 about 2% less ozone separating sunlovers from the object of their devotions than there had been in 1969.

Why did none of this emerge before? How had scientists diligently collected this data for almost twenty years without noticing the trend? The answer, Watson admitted, was salutary. The scientists operating the ground monitors had devoted too much time to plugging the data into their models of what they thought was happening to the ozone layer, and too little time sifting the data itself for trends. Indeed, their desire to produce statistically tidy graphs had meant they weeded out the very data which showed the decline in ozone.

Watson said that since nobody was looking for a seasonal fall in ozone levels, nobody looked at the data season by season. Investigators simply averaged all the data taken during a year. Then, since fluctuations appeared greatest in winter and least in summer, they weighted the annual averages to take more account of summer readings. (More readings were taken in summer in any case, because the weather is nicer.) So the winter falls did not have much effect on annual averages. Finally, since fluctuations were smallest nearer the equator, researchers weighted the global averages in favour of stations in the tropics — just where, we now know, the dip in ozone levels was least marked.

They could not have done a better job of obscuring the trend if they had tried. It was not until 1986, in the wake of Farman's findings, that somebody began to look again at the raw data from one measuring station, Arosa in the Swiss Alps, the oldest continuous monitor. Then the truth began to unravel.

A WHIFF OF CHLORINE IN THE ARCTIC

In January 1989, after this book went to press, Watson's team, armed with some $10 million from NASA's coffers, intended to fly its spy plane, the ER2, from Spitzbergen into the cold winter air above the Arctic. The aim was to explore whether the same chemistry that is creating the Antarctic ozone hole is busy excavating a hole over the Arctic. One man had already taken a peek. Jim Anderson from Harvard, who had spent much of 1988 planning the Arctic trip, sent the ER2 on a preliminary mission into the Arctic Circle in February 1988. There he found raised levels of chlorine monoxide, the 'smoking gun' of the Antarctic.

'The concentrations were only five or seven times the levels further south,' Anderson said. Inside the Antarctic ozone hole, they were 100 to 500 times higher than normal. But his flight only took instruments to 61°N, hundreds of kilometres further away from the pole than the Antarctic readings were taken. 'We flew over Great Slave Lake in Canada,' he told me. 'We were kissing the edge of the polar vortex.' There are some stratospheric clouds over the Arctic in winter, but the plane did not reach them. The following January, he was planning to fly to 84°N, tracking pockets of the coldest air around, looking for stratospheric clouds and searching for signs of chlorine monoxide eating ozone within them.

The Arctic vortex is less contained than the Antarctic version, with pockets of air from Siberia and Canada breaking into and out of it. That means the critical temperatures at which ice crystals form are probably found only sporadically. But in 1988 there was growing interest in the idea that other solid particles in the stratosphere could trigger the reactions which cause the runaway destruction of ozone. Top of the

31

list were aerosols of sulphuric acid, which are present in the stratosphere all round the world throughout the year. Sulphuric acid forms naturally in the air from gases given off by volcanoes and marine organisms. But industrial nations have doubled the global load in recent decades by releasing sulphur dioxide when burning fossil fuels. Most of it falls as acid rain, but some probably reaches the stratosphere. This possibility was an alarming thought left hanging in the air during conferences on the ozone hole during 1988.

A critical question for the future of the ozone layer is how much of the loss of stratospheric ozone now evident at most latitudes outside the tropics is a product of chemical reactions at those latitudes, and how much is a dilution effect from the destruction taking place over the poles. It could take some years to sort that out. Meanwhile, scientists are sure of one thing: the destruction of ozone round the globe is proceeding much faster than predicted by the models that underpinned the UNEP's case at Montreal.

Watson warned in 1988 that those predictions were:

> two or three times too low. Chlorine levels over Antarctica today are around three parts per billion. That chlorine was put into the atmosphere at least a decade ago. Plenty more is on its way. Under the Montreal Protocol we can expect levels [of chlorine] there to reach six or seven parts per billion. We would need a 95% cut in CFC production to get back to chlorine levels that we had in 1960, before the loss of ozone began. Even then, the hole would probably last for 50 years.

Farman is even more pessimistic. In an article in *New Scientist* in 1987, he warned:

> We are putting CFCs into the atmosphere five times faster than natural processes can dispose of them. If emissions ceased tomorrow, about a third of the CFC-11 will still be there in 65 years' time, while the corresponding period for CFC-12 is 120 years. The protocol as it stands has committed us to an increase in stratospheric chlorine to about

three times the present level by 2020. That is, to some ten times the amount present before the use of CFCs became widespread.

Giving evidence to the Environment Committee of the House of Commons in London in March 1988, Farman called for a cut in CFC emissions of 85%. Rowland agrees: 'Montreal was an essential first step. But it is nothing like enough.'

The nations that approved the Montreal Protocol are committed to a review of the science of ozone depletion in 1990. It was clear from the day they signed the protocol that they would by then be under strong pressure to toughen their stance. Perhaps public pressure will force action. The major supermarket chains in Britain stopped stocking aerosols containing CFCs during 1988, long before the government decided to act. And the Tasmanian state government in Australia, feeling closest to the ozone hole, announced an almost complete ban on dangerous products containing CFCs. These actions show that, when a risk to our planet is demonstrated unequivocally by scientists, the public and governments will respond. But the other lesson is that the process of scientific discovery and public education may be too slow.

Watson warned that an increase in the activity of the Sun in 1989 seemed likely to bring relief to the ozone layer for a year or two. This is because extra solar radiation encourages the formation of new ozone in the stratosphere. Certainly, the ozone hole was less intense in 1988 than for several years. But as the Sun's activity falls again in the mid-1990s, in accordance with its eleven-year cycle of activity, Watson predicted an even deeper hole over Antarctica.

Whatever action we take now, we are, as Watson put it, 'almost certainly stuck with the ozone hole for the next 50 years'. To forestall perils, we need to think ahead more imaginatively, study our data more carefully and act more boldly.

2

HOW THINGS BEGAN

The solid planets — Mercury, Venus, Earth and Mars — form an inner ring around the Sun. They were probably created with the Solar System about 4.6 billion years ago, perhaps from cosmic debris left over from the Big Bang. From the start, the planets were more than lumps of rock. They were hot. The Earth had a largely molten core, made mostly of nickel-iron, and an outer mantle of silicate, topped by a thin crust.

Above the crust, our atmosphere formed only slowly, fed by gases released through volcanoes from the interior. This early atmosphere was probably made up largely of carbon dioxide with water vapour and some nitrogen, rather like the atmospheres round Mars and Venus today. (Mercury is too small for its gravity to hold an atmosphere.) As the aeons passed, however, these three planets evolved in different ways. The result today is a dead Venus, a living Earth and, most intriguingly, a Mars that is now dead but which might have had life during its first billion years.

Some planetary scientists have dubbed the Earth the 'Goldilocks planet'. The idea comes from the story of 'Goldilocks and the Three Bears'. When Goldilocks tasted porridge at the house of the three bears, she found one bowl (Venus) too hot, one (Mars) too cold, but the other (Earth) just right. The Goldilocks theory holds that, purely by chance, life evolved on Earth because the climate, in the words of the story, was 'just right'. That has been the

34

conventional view until recently. But a team of Americans which began its studies at the University of Michigan is shedding new light on the early history of the three planets. The team's leading lights, Jim Walker and Jim Kasting (who now works for NASA), say that Mars, Earth and Venus started with remarkably similar atmospheres dominated by carbon dioxide and some water vapour. What determined the fate of the three planets was the fate of these gases.

Carbon dioxide is a 'greenhouse gas'. Like the glass panes in a greenhouse, it lets in the sunlight, but traps the heat reflected back from the ground. The more carbon dioxide there is in the air, the warmer a planet becomes. The surface of the Earth is currently about 35°C warmer than it would be without its blanket of carbon dioxide.

Both Earth and Mars had liquid water in the early days. Nobody is sure whether Venus had water, but, if it did, intense sunlight must soon have turned it to water vapour. No liquid water meant no rain. Rain removed carbon dioxide gradually from the Earth and Mars, but on rainless Venus, a thick warm shroud of carbon dioxide has persisted to this day.

Meanwhile, water vapour in Venus's clouds reflects so much sunlight back into space that, despite the planet being bombarded with almost twice as much of the Sun's radiation as the Earth, the surface of Venus receives less heat than our own planet. Temperatures on Venus average 460°C. But without the 'greenhouse effect' of the carbon dioxide and water vapour, Venus would actually be cooler than the Earth. Climatologists call the fate of Venus the 'runaway greenhouse'.

On Mars, the rain slowly dissolved the carbon dioxide in the air and deposited it on the ground as dilute carbonic acid. While the Martian atmosphere is still made up mostly of carbon dioxide, it has precious little atmosphere at all. Most of the carbon is in the rocks. This transfer of carbon from air to rocks changed the Martian climate for ever.

Today, with only a thin blanket of carbon dioxide, Mars is a cold lifeless desert. 'Its surface looks like Utah or Arizona,' says Chris McKay, a Mars-watcher at NASA. There is no longer any rain. The famous 'canals' on Mars, which astronomers have wondered about for decades, no longer run with water as they did during the first billion or so years of Mars's existence. By washing carbon dioxide out of the air, rain has cooled the planet to an average of minus 60°C. The water has all turned to ice.

Says McKay: 'The environment on early Mars was comparable to the early Earth in all the biologically important parameters over a time period comparable to the origin of life on Earth.' In other words, life was as likely to develop there as on Earth. Rocks older than any found today on Earth are probably still exposed there. When new remotely controlled vehicles trundle across the surface of Mars during the 1990s, those rocks may yield answers to the questions: was there ever life on Mars, and if so why did it perish? This might help answer another rather more parochial question: why did life on Earth both develop and flourish?

On Earth we have escaped both the 'runaway greenhouse' of Venus and the destruction of the greenhouse that took place on Mars. Our greenhouse remains remarkably comfortable, keeping a relatively constant temperature since the earliest days. This is surprising since the Sun's radiation has become roughly a third more intense since the first billion years of our planet. The theories about how the Earth's atmosphere maintained its temperature go to the heart of current thinking about how our planet operates, and set the scene for thinking about what might happen as we take over the controls.

SEARCH FOR THE THERMOSTAT

If the atmosphere on the Earth four billion years ago had been anything like it is today, the planet would have been frozen. The Sun was too weak to support life. Yet, if anything, the Earth was hotter then than it is today. Geologists have yet to find evidence of glaciers or ice packs before about 2.7 billion years ago. The puzzle of why the Earth was not cooler then was first pointed out in 1971 by George Mullen and his colleague, Carl Sagan, the now-famous astronomer who was director of the Laboratory for Planetary Studies at Cornell University in the US. The two men guessed that the greenhouse effect must have trapped more heat in the early Earth's atmosphere than it does today. The planet had a thicker blanket against the cold. They suggested that the blanket was made of ammonia. Later investigators showed that sunlight would have swiftly broken down ammonia into its constituent parts, hydrogen and nitrogen. (The conversion could have been completed in less than 40 years, according to one estimate.) Today, the consensus is that carbon dioxide did the job. One intriguing calculation is that in total there are similar amounts of carbon on the surfaces of Venus and the Earth. On Venus it is all in the atmosphere, but on Earth more than 99% of it is bound up in rock. Even so, there is enough left in the air to maintain the equability of our climate.

The big problem is to discover a mechanism that might gradually have syphoned carbon dioxide from the air to the rocks for over four billion years, at just the right rate to keep the planet's temperature between roughly 15 and 30°C. We are looking for nothing less than a planetary thermostat. We are looking, moreover, for a thermostat which would work on Earth, but which failed to work on Mars. There are two theories.

One, from Walker and Kasting, is based on geology. The other much more controversial idea suggests that living organisms have harnessed geology to create a world to suit themselves. The father of this latter idea is Jim Lovelock, a British scientist-cum-inventor who came up with his revolutionary idea while working for NASA on ways to establish whether Mars contained signs of life.

Lovelock began the debate in the early 1970s with the breathtaking suggestion that the Earth was 'alive'. It operated like a 'superorganism', he said, 'exhibiting the behaviour of a single organism, even a living creature'. The science establishment was scandalized. His papers were rejected for several years by the leading journals, such as *Science* and *Nature*. A few editors, such as Bernard Dixon at *New Scientist* and Bert Bolin, the revered Swedish meteorologist who edited a small journal called *Tellus*, published his papers. But most could not cope with Lovelock's ideas or his insistence on giving his 'superorganism' a mythical name.

The name was 'Gaia', the Earth goddess of ancient Greece. William Golding, who later won a Nobel prize for literature, had suggested it.

The idea has had a bumpy ride. But by the late 1980s, Lovelock's work was again welcome in *Nature* and *Science*, and in March 1988 both journals reported a conference organized by the American Geophysical Union to discuss the Gaia hypothesis.

Gaian ideas have infused the work of many investigators into the behaviour of our planet. But Lovelock's influence has been most profound in the search for the global thermostat. He pointed out that tiny plant-like organisms, called phytoplankton and found almost everywhere in the oceans, consume carbon dioxide to make their skeletons.

If, as the Sun grew in strength and the Earth warmed up, these plankton became more numerous, they would consume more carbon dioxide. To feed their requirements the ocean would need to absorb more of the gas from the atmosphere, something which it can freely do. The plankton would reduce the greenhouse effect. When they died, their carbon-containing remains would fall to the bottom of the sea, forming carbonate rocks, thus removing carbon from the world of living organisms for, at the least, millions of years.

This is Lovelock's living planet in operation and he likes to compare it with the human body. He believes science is on the verge of discovering the metabolism of the Earth, much as physicians such as William Harvey discovered the basic workings of the human body 400 years ago. That is why he calls his Gaian science 'geophysiology'.

Lovelock's idea of a biological thermostat assumes that in a warmer world there really would be more phytoplankton in the sea. In the modern world, the growth of plankton in the oceans is usually limited not by temperature but by the amount of nutrients, such as nitrogen and phosphorus, on which they can feed. But, says Lovelock, a warmer Earth would be a wetter Earth because a hotter Sun would evaporate more water from the oceans. More rain would fall, some of it on land. This would increase the flow of water from the land back into the oceans. With the water come the nutrients that feed the plankton.

If this mechanism overshot and the Earth began to cool, it would swing into reverse. In a cooler world, says Lovelock, the climate would be drier and fewer nutrients would wash into the sea. There would be fewer phytoplankton. The oceans' ability to snatch carbon dioxide from the air would diminish and the release of carbon dioxide from the planet's depths through volcanic eruptions would slowly rebuild the greenhouse. Temperatures would rise again.

This is an appealing idea. But there are some obvious gaps in the argument. First, there remains no firm evidence that there would have been more plankton in a warmer world. Stephen Schneider, who organized the 1988 Gaia conference but who is still a sceptic, points out that there were no phytoplankton for the first three billion years or so of the planet's existence. 'Phytoplankton as it exists today could not have been the primary carbon sink during the three-billion-year period in which simpler life dominated and the Sun was continuing to heat up. Perhaps bacteria participated, but the mechanisms ... have yet to be shown.' Lovelock has a lot more work to do in order to demonstrate his case.

LIFE AS A GEOLOGICAL FORCE

While Lovelock was developing his ideas, more conventional planetary scientists were also looking for a thermostat to control the greenhouse effect. Walker, Kasting and another colleague from Michigan, Paul Hays, saw no reason for life itself to be running things and proposed an alternative system for stabilizing temperatures. Their theory is also based on carbon dioxide, but it is run by geology.

The starting point for their thermostat, as outlined in a paper in 1981, is the fallout of carbon dioxide from the atmosphere on to land. Walker et al. pointed out, like Lovelock, that a warmer world will have more rain. More rain, they said, will remove more carbon dioxide from the air. That will bring temperatures back down again. This carbon dioxide, brought to the ground as dilute carbonic acid, weathers rocks by combining with the silicate materials which make up most of the Earth's crust, and flows with them to the sea. There the carbon will eventually form sedimentary rocks on the sea floor, and so be removed from the scene. This much sounds exactly like what might have happened on Mars.

It is a one-way process. But a thermostat must have a way of supplying more carbon dioxide to the air to warm it up when necessary. Here Walker introduces plate tectonics, the great movements of continental plates across the Earth's crust, i.e. continental drift.

Kasting outlined this process in more detail in an article in *Scientific American* in 1988. 'As the millenniums pass, the sea floor spreads, carrying these [carbon] sediments to the margins of the continents. There the sea floor slides under the land masses and turns downward towards the interior of the planet.' This sounds like the ultimate burial for carbon dioxide and if that was all that happened we could have ended up like Mars after all. But, he goes on, 'as the sediment is subducted and subjected to rising temperature and pressure, calcium carbonate reacts . . . releasing gaseous carbon dioxide. The gas then re-enters the atmosphere by way of mid-ocean ridges or, more violently, through volcanic eruptions.'

This grand progression of carbon dioxide is called the carbonate–silicate cycle. And, say Walker and Kasting, it will respond to changes in the atmosphere to control the temperature of the planet. If the planet warms, more rain falls and the carbon dioxide in the air diminishes. 'If the oceans ever froze over completely, rainfall would come to a virtual halt and carbon dioxide would build up in the atmosphere' as it slowly vented from the rocks beneath. At current rates, they suggest, you could, by this process, raise the Earth's temperature by 50°C within twenty million years.

On Mars, rain has removed carbon dioxide from the air and all the water has frozen. But no carbon dioxide has returned to the atmosphere to warm the planet again. Why not? There is no thermostat on Mars. That, said Kasting, is because Mars is too small to have a crust made up of mobile plates. Mars has only half the diameter of Earth. It does not contain enough internal heat to cause the churning motions in the interior of the planet that sustain the plate tectonics of the Earth, so its crust is a single mass. No plate tectonics means no carbonate–silicate cycle. And that, Walker and Kasting conclude, is why Mars is cold, dry and dead, while the Earth is warm, wet and alive.

This is dramatic stuff. The great geological processes of the planet appear to dwarf biological processes, after all. But Lovelock was quick to respond. Before Walker's paper was published, he had submitted his reply. It came out in April 1982. Lovelock argued that, in the current world, life is intimately wound up with the supposedly inorganic thermostat suggested by Walker. Living organisms help speed up the processes of weathering and take charge of the process by which carbon works its way to the bottom of the oceans. Life controls the carbonate–silicate cycle, he said.

The debate was still in full flood when Walker, Kasting, Lovelock and the Gaians crossed swords at the Gaia conference in 1988. In soils, said Lovelock, micro-organisms determine the rate of weathering. They are constantly at work decomposing dead plants, and in the process they maintain concentrations of carbon dioxide typically 20 to 40 times higher than in the atmosphere. This increases the amount of carbonic acid in the soil and speeds up the process of weathering many times. Moreover, if you warm the microbes up, they work faster. David Schwartzman, a geologist from Howard University in Washington DC, sided with Lovelock. He told the conference that organic acids from soil microbes and, in the tropics, formic acid from ants, seem to be more important than carbonic acid in weathering processes.

Nobody in San Diego doubted that Walker's thermostat could work. But Lovelock believes that living organisms have harnessed it to meet their own needs. 'The biota seems to act as a sensor of temperature change and as an amplifier to magnify the rate of weathering of the silicate rocks and pumping of carbon dioxide from the air,' he said. Life, for Lovelock, is a potent geological force.

In the oceans, too, living things control the flow of carbon. Marine organisms speed up the fallout of carbon to the ocean floor. They draw carbon from the atmosphere, through the surface layers of the oceans to the ocean floor. Marine biologists call this the 'biological pump'. In effect it means that organisms dictate the ability of the ocean to absorb carbon dioxide from the air.

Walker was on the defensive in San Diego. 'Agreed,' he said, 'on the present Earth, most precipitation [of carbon on to the sea floor] is biological. But there is an inorganic mechanism waiting in the wings to take over.' So what would happen if life disappeared overnight and Walker's mechanism had to work on its own? In this 'Strangelove world' there would, all agreed, be a gigantic lurch in the system. Without living organisms, Walker's carbonate–silicate cycle would slow down drastically. Eventually, the system would reach a new equilibrium in which the weathering of rocks on land would be much slower and less carbon dioxide would pass from the air to the sea.

Both sides seemed to agree that the world would be perhaps 10°C warmer, but they put a different gloss on it. Walker told the conference that, while living organisms could take part in his cycle, 'the fundamental controls on atmospheric carbon dioxide levels are physical rather than biological.' If life had never developed, the world would have been a hotter place, but 'the Earth would have remained habitable even if it had never been inhabited.'

Lovelock sees it differently. Today's temperatures are kept down, despite the hotter Sun, by life and 'this is consistent with the Gaia hypothesis'. Living organisms have evolved, Lovelock told the conference, to 'use geologically driven processes to provide additional temperature stabilization'. There is, after all, a kind of consensus here.

THE BREATH OF LIFE

The Gaian idea is bringing new insights into our understanding of the evolution of the Earth. Awakened by Lovelock, biologists are looking for signs of organisms that alter the planet. And they are finding those signs everywhere. Nobody knows quite when life began on Earth, or how. But the first evidence comes from signs of primitive bugs tinkering with their environment. The earliest known rocks are carbon sediments uncovered in Greenland. They are about 3.8 billion years old and appear to have been laid down in bands. To geologists such as Stan Awramik from the University of California at Santa Barbara, the layering suggests that micro-organisms were at work processing these sediments on the ocean floor.

But the best early evidence of life comes from rocks in Australia. The tell-tale rocks are stromatolites, layered structures made of calcium carbonate and found in shallow waters. They look rather like cauliflowers. Similar structures are still produced today by blue-green algae, single-celled aquatic plants which collect in massive mat-like colonies and process carbonate material. Today, that material is usually the skeletons of dead plankton, falling to the bottom of the sea. The algae deposit the carbonate in distinctive layers. As each layer forms, the algae colonize it, ready to collect the aquatic fallout to create a new layer.

Awramik, who discovered many of the earliest organisms, says that they were sophisticated beasts. They were 'sensitive to light and could move rapidly in order to stay at the interface between water and sediment'. In a primitive way, then, more than 3.5 billion years ago, these algae were involving themselves in the fundamental planetary process of cycling carbon. They had placed a hand on the planetary thermostat.

These algae were also engaged in photosynthesis, con-verting sunlight into chemical energy. Some of them, it seems, created oxygen along the way, just as modern plants do. They began the long process by which oxygen took its place in the operation of the planet.

Without living organisms, there could be no more than a tiny amount of oxygen in the atmosphere. Without oxygen, any but the simplest forms of life could not survive on Earth. This sounds a pleasant enough symbiosis, and very Gaian, but for one thing: the organisms that first created oxygen were gradually poisoned by it. In creating an atmosphere dominated by oxygen, many of those early primitive organisms found themselves, around two billion years ago, committing collective suicide. They had inherited an environment in which hydrogen dominated and in which oxide compounds, which dominate the chemistry of our world today, shed their oxygen. Rust turned back to iron. In its place, they created a world in which oxygen dominates and elements take up oxygen. After that, iron rusted. About two billion years ago, oxygen had saturated the oceans and began to bubble up out of the sea and accumulate in the atmosphere.

The entire biology of the planet changed with the chemistry. The dominant micro-organisms up to that point had needed an oxygen-free environment. Most must have died out. The survivors headed for permanent exile in the bottoms of swamps, the polyps of coral reefs, the guts of termites — anywhere that was free of oxygen. It was pollution on a gigantic scale. Lovelock calls it 'probably the most critical period in all the history of life on Earth ... an almost fatal catastrophe for early life'. It is also a rather critical issue for Gaian ideas. Gaian theory says that organisms work in harmony to create the best possible environment for themselves. So why would one form of life sacrifice itself to allow new forms to evolve? As Schneider put it: 'Why, if it was in the interests of the early biota to control their environment, would they produce oxygen, a poison for themselves?'

Modern blue-green algae may offer a clue. They can survive both with and without oxygen. Their ancestors, the builders of stromatolites, may have been the first beneficiaries of the great change in the planet's environment. Since they must have been one of the prime producers of oxygen, they might, by a process of natural selection, have engineered the entire catastrophe to wipe out their rivals. When the great pollution came, the fittest, the blue-green algae, survived.

If Gaia means anything, we must conclude that, at that moment, blue-green algae were in charge of the planet. They were the General Motors of their day. What was good for blue-green algae was, by definition, good for life.

Once the brave new oxygenated world was set up, life could step up a gear. Organisms that could survive in the new world could create energy much more efficiently. They could do away with old-fashioned fermentation, which, as any amateur wine-maker will know, happens only without oxygen. Instead, they took up a new metabolism called respiration, which requires oxygen. It is several times more efficient than fermentation.

Around this time, too, a new type of cell made its appearance. Cells of the old order were called prokaryotes, had no nucleus and could operate without oxygen. Bacteria are a modern example. New-order cells, called eukaryotes, were larger, had nuclei and appear in the fossil record from about 1.4 billion years ago. They required oxygen to work because a key protein, actomyosin, which allows chromosomes within the nucleus to split during cell division, can only form when there is oxygen around. The arrival of eukaryotic cells was, many biologists argue, the critical breakthrough in the evolution of modern plants and animals. 'The differences between these groups are far greater than the differences between plants and animals,' says Lynn Margulis of Boston University. The new-order cells, coupled with the new techniques of creating energy by respiration, became the building blocks for organisms with many cells.

This biological revolution was happening deep within the oceans. The upper layers of the oceans and the atmosphere remained a lethal environment, even for oxygen-guzzlers. The reason was that the ultraviolet radiation from the Sun damages the proteins and acids that are essential to the operation of living cells. A few metres of sea water filters out ultraviolet light. Today, so does the ozone layer. But, in the early days of the planet, there was no ozone layer. It formed slowly, perhaps only within the past 500 million years. As oxygen accumulated slowly in the atmosphere, it fed enough oxygen into the upper atmosphere to begin the formation of the ozone shield.

At that point, life could safely venture closer to the surface of the water. There, organisms could absorb more of the Sun's energy, accelerating the pace of life. Eventually, some 400 million years ago, living organisms first ventured on to land. Something like the modern world had begun.

DEATH OF THE DINOSAURS

The 1980s were the years when the idea that nature progresses slowly and predictably gave way to more alarming ideas about flips, lurches, jolts and cataclysms. Physicists investigating the bizarre worlds of particle physics and cosmology, of nuclear explosions and supernovae, gave up the cosy notion of slow, steady development long ago. But many biologists stuck with it, as did climatologists, oceanographers and others watching over the progress of life and our planet.

Philosophers may develop theories about why the natural world suddenly seemed a more dangerous place. But in the Earth sciences two events seem to have triggered the process. One was the sudden opening of the ozone hole. The other was the realization that some cataclysm shook the Earth on the day (and it may not have been much longer than a day) when the dinosaurs died out.

Walter Alvarez and his father Luis began the 1980s with a bang that is still reverberating through the science journals at the end of the decade. Luis was a physicist working in California. Sudden events were his life's work. He had helped build the atomic bomb during the Second World War and later gained a Nobel prize for his studies of extremely short-lived subatomic particles called resonance particles. Walter was a geologist at the University of California at Berkeley. He took the flak.

In June 1980, the father and son team published a paper in *Science* proposing that an object from outer space collided with the Earth 65 million years ago, causing the sudden extinction of the dinosaurs and many other creatures of land, sea and air. 'Most of my colleagues were scandalized by the idea. They believed in smooth progressions of history,' Walter Alvarez remembered some years later. 'But the fact is there is now a lot of evidence of an impact somewhere on the Earth of an object 10 kilometres or so across. It hit the Earth at a speed of between 10 and 40 kilometres per second, depositing 100 million megatonnes of energy.' That is, if you can imagine it, the equivalent of exploding 100 million million tonnes of TNT, or a million times the total annual seismic release from earthquakes.

Behind the object, during its brief and violent journey through the atmosphere, a vacuum formed. In front of it, air became so compressed that temperatures briefly reached several times those in the heart of the Sun.

Michael Rampino from New York University takes up the

story. 'The impact caused a crater 200 kilometres wide and 40 kilometres deep. It penetrated right through the crust of the Earth, causing major volcanic flows.' Alvarez says, 'the impact was similar to a giant fission bomb.' It would have blasted 60 times its own mass of rock into the air. 'Thirty seconds after the impact solid rock was 40 kilometres above the Earth's surface.' Much of the rock was blasted into space, from where it returned to Earth as glassy droplets of rock. The rest formed a blanket of debris, blocking out the Sun for months on end.

Not surprisingly, many geologists have gone looking for the crater that might have been left by such a blast. If, as Rampino thinks, the meteorite fell into the ocean, then the crater will have been subducted beneath the continents by now. If it is on land, Michael Kunk at the US Geological Survey suggests the Manson crater in Iowa. The crater is the right age and, at 32 kilometres across, passably big. But there are other candidates in the US and the Soviet Union. They seem to form a line across the Earth. Perhaps a large object broke up into several pieces as it approached Earth.

The best evidence for the occurrence of an impact from a meteorite, as the Alvarezes' paper made clear in 1980, is the discovery of large amounts of a metal called iridium in rocks previously dated as having been laid down 65 million years ago. Iridium is one of a group of metals similar to platinum. It is rare on Earth, but found much more abundantly on extraterrestrial objects such as comets and asteroids. Deep-sea limestones exposed in Italy, Denmark and New Zealand reveal increases in iridium of respectively 30, 160 and 20 times in layers formed at the time the dinosaurs died. More recently, geologists have found 'shock-disrupted quartz' round the world at precisely the same place in the geological record. This type of rock is apparently unique to places hit by extraterrestrial objects.

The main alternative theory about the catastrophe that destroyed the dinosaurs postulates a major outbreak of volcanic activity round the world. One version is that between 68 and 66 million years ago northern India was a volcanic cauldron, spewing a sheet of basalt 2,000 metres thick across the Western Ghats south of Bombay. Thus perhaps it was volcanoes that put dust into the air rather than the impact of a meteorite. But the advocates of the volcanic theory have so far failed to find shock-disrupted quartz in volcanic rocks.

It was not only the dinosaurs that disappeared 65 million years ago. Virtually all the plants on land died out too, as did 90% of the plankton in the sea, all of the reptiles of the sea and air (such as pterodactyls), and every animal on land weighing more than about 25 kilograms, including, of course, the dinosaurs. The surviving animals, including our own mammalian ancestors, probably survived by grubbing around feeding on insects and rotting vegetation.

Clearly something rather bothersome has happened to the 'steady as she goes' school of history. In trying to uncover the forces that a collision would have unleashed (and to establish whether these forces can be made to fit the patterns of extinctions), scientists have been able to indulge their wildest fantasies, and still probably understate what was going on.

Walter Alvarez drew on the evidence of what happened when Krakatoa, a volcanic island in the East Indies, blew up in 1883. It threw eighteen square kilometres of rock into the atmosphere, of which a quarter reached the stratosphere. There it stayed for more than two years causing brilliant sunsets round the world. Alvarez reckoned that his comet would have sent a thousand times as much rock into the skies. It would, he said, have spread roughly a gram of dust across every square centimetre of the stratosphere. Forget about the sunsets, though. It would have blotted out the Sun, turning day into night for several years and sending temperatures plunging. After the publication of new ideas about the climatic consequences of nuclear war, this theory became known as the 'nuclear winter' theory.

Since then, every scientist with an eye for disasters has been poking round the evidence looking for clues to support his or her own pet theory. Most involve the horrible things that would have happened after the dust returned to Earth. Many popular themes find a home: acid rain, holes in the ozone layer, the greenhouse effect. Even Gaians get a look in.

At the California Institute of Technology (Caltech) they have fired four extremely powerful guns into blocks of limestone of the kind that make up much of the Earth's surface. John O'Keefe and his colleagues simulated with these guns the effect of a meteorite hitting Earth at a speed of up to six kilometres a second. They concluded that:

If an asteroid or a comet with a radius of 50 kilometres struck the Earth at a four-kilometre-thick carbonate-rich layer [of rock] there would be an immediate hundred-fold increase in the amount of carbon dioxide in the atmosphere. This would lead to an increase in average temperatures of about 20°C within only ten days, due to the greenhouse effect ... The increased levels would persist for about 10,000 years.

So maybe the dinosaurs boiled to death, rather than froze.

The demise of sea life 65 million years ago is almost more remarkable than the disappearance of the dinosaurs. What caused this 'Strangelove ocean'? We know that a drastic warming of the surface layers of the oceans would allow less carbon dioxide to dissolve in the water. So perhaps the plankton ran out of carbon to build their shells. That would explain why the 'calcareous plankton', which build shells of calcium carbonate, suffered worst, disappearing almost entirely. Other marine organisms would have starved without plankton to eat. Without life, the oceans' ability to absorb carbon dioxide from the air would have fallen further, thus exacerbating the greenhouse warming.

While the Californians considered the impact of carbon being blasted into the air by a meteorite, Ronald Prinn at the Massachusetts Institute of Technology developed his 'super-acid rain' theory. He said that the sudden heating of the atmosphere during the arrival of the meteorite would have created masses of nitric oxide in the air. The nitric oxide would have converted both to nitrogen dioxide, a gas that poisons plants and animals, and to nitric acid. He suggests that 'a meteoritic impact made the global atmosphere a thousand times more polluted than the worst modern smog, and that the precipitation of nitric acid caused the extinction.'

This super-acid rainfall 'would destroy much of the biosphere'. It would have made the upper layers of the oceans so acid that the skeletons of calcareous organisms would have dissolved. Animals could have escaped the acid fallout if they had hibernated. Eggs laid in burrows would have survived.

Paul Crutzen of the Max Planck Institute in West Germany is a prodigious generator of ideas. He first proposed the idea that a 'nuclear winter' might follow a nuclear war. Crutzen has adopted the super-acid rain idea and argues that the liberation of masses of nitrogen oxides could have both accentuated the greenhouse effect and eaten away at the ozone layer. The acid fallout would also have mobilized from soils toxic metals such as aluminium. These ought now to show up in the rocks of that era.

Evidence backing Prinn's idea comes with a study of isotopes of strontium in sea water, as revealed in fossil rocks. The graph of the ratio of strontium 87 to strontium 86 showed a sudden 'spike' 65 million years ago. Strontium 87 comes from the land and researchers suggest that this spike may reveal a sudden increase in the erosion of rocks caused, perhaps, by super-acid rainfall.

Another after-effect of the meteorite's impact seems to have been forest fires, which raged across the planet engulfing any trees that survived the heat and shockwaves of the initial impact. Analysis of rocks laid down at the time suggest that about 100 billion tonnes of soot piled up on the ground. Fires sufficient to create that amount of soot would also have led, says Crutzen, to the accumulation of 15 times more carbon dioxide in the atmosphere than is present today, along with 4,000 times more carbon monoxide, 30 times more methane and 7 times more nitrous oxide in the air than today. These gases are greenhouse gases.

Finally, Rampino and his vigorous young colleague from New York, Tyler Volk, have picked up a Gaian idea to suggest another mechanism for heating the planet. With most of the plankton in the sea dead, there would be less dimethyl sulphide (DMS) around. As we shall see later, this gas, excreted by plankton, plays an important part in the formation of clouds. Once the blanket of soot and debris had settled on Earth, a Strangelove ocean would have had fewer clouds above it to reflect the Sun's heat. This, the New Yorkers suggest, 'could have produced a rapid global warming of 6°C or more'.

None of these consequences are proven. But all fit some part of the fossil evidence and all are plausible. If nothing else, they demonstrate the range and intensity of responses, both biological and geological, that our planet has to catastrophic events. And they provide clues to the sort of runaway reactions that could follow our own blunderings in the cockpit of spaceship Earth.

Fossil records suggest that in the years after the impact, some 70% of species disappeared. But every cloud — even a black affair obliterating the Sun in a super-acid smog — has a silver lining. Crutzen says: 'Many species could not survive. Those that did must have enjoyed a paradise.' Within a few thousand years, it appears, a single species of fern had revived so well that it covered more than 90% of the land. Stromatolites, which had been in decline since their golden age some two billion years before, made a brief comeback. Other forms of life took longer to revive. The fallout on the sea floor of calcium carbonate from the skeletons of marine animals did not recover for almost a million years.

Perhaps what came after was better than what went before. All mammalian chauvinists must agree that mammals were an improvement on dinosaurs. Would mammals have stood a chance of development without the mass extinction of 65 million years ago? Very likely not. Walter Alvarez asks:

Is catastrophe essential to evolution? Evolution seems to slow down as ecological niches for various life forms are filled. But we know that evolution proceeded very fast after the disaster that ended the dinosaurs.

It is increasingly clear that the date when dinosaurs met their destiny was only the most recent of many in prehistory when cataclysmic disaster overtook life on Earth. It was not even the worst. Of the five great crises and many more lesser ones that show up in the fossil records of the past 600 million years, the worst was about 250 million years ago. Then, according to one estimate, 96% of species disappeared. Were these events also the result of extraterrestrial impacts? The evidence is tenuous, but the search for tell-tale signs of iridium is under way. Chinese researchers claim to have found a lot of iridium throughout southern China in rocks laid down 250 million years ago. Soviet scientists report finding shocked quartz in rocks of that age. There is even a candidate for the crater left by a meteorite on arrival — the 70-kilometre Manicouagan crater in Quebec.

Intriguingly, some researchers claim to see a pattern in the sparse findings of high levels of iridium discovered so far. And the pattern ties in with the even more interesting suggestion by statisticians that mass extinctions seem to appear roughly once every 26 million years. David Raup and John Sepkoski of the University of Chicago point out that the eight main extinctions in the past 268 million years were respectively, 248, 219, 194, 144, 91, 65, 38 and 11 million years ago.

Why should there be such regularity in apparently random events? Some researchers, like Lovelock, feel the need to invoke mythology. One idea is called 'Nemesis', after the Greek goddess of justice and vengeance. It suggests that the Sun has a dark companion star, invisible to us, which rotates around it every 26 million years. This companion star drags comets into the path of the Earth at a certain point in its orbit. Sometimes the comets hit us.

Michael Rampino, not to be outdone, has come up with 'Shiva', the Hindu god of destruction and rebirth. He suggests that, every 26 million years or so, our Solar System moves into an area of the galaxy where cosmic forces drag comets which usually circle harmlessly beyond the planets across our path. Why Shiva? Well, if the new evolutionists are right in saying that catastrophes are necessary to keep evolution going, then life on Earth needs these comets to progress. Destruction and rebirth are inseparably linked. Perhaps Gaia needs Shiva.

3

SHIFTING SANDS

Jericho was the first town the Israelites saw when they crossed into the Promised Land. It was established 10,000 years ago in the Jordan valley, as the last ice age abated. It is probably the oldest town in the world and its inhabitants were fed on cereals planted in fields that surrounded the town. Today, those fields have turned to barren scrub. It is not just the walls that have fallen since Jericho's heyday. The local ecology has collapsed as well.

Throughout the Middle East and far into Asia, the fields that nurtured the first civilizations have followed a similar path to destruction as salt has poisoned their fields. Susa in Mesopotamia thrived on a sophisticated system of irrigated fields. The land is now 10,000 square kilometres of salt-encrusted badlands over which Iran and Iraq fought tank battles through the 1980s. The Iranian river of Karkheh passes through the ruins of ancient Susa before pouring into countless abandoned canals and trickling into the sand. Susa and the other city states that rose in Mesopotamia 6,000 years ago once fed 25 million people and had food left to sell. Most of those fields were poisoned by salt that arrived in tiny quantities, dissolved in the irrigation waters. The salt built up slowly until nothing would grow. The land around the rivers Tigris and Euphrates, once known as the 'fertile crescent', is now almost completely infertile. The population of the area has halved, yet much of the food has to be imported.

53

In the American southwest, the decline of ancient Indian civilizations is blamed on salt. Salt is a scourge of most irrigation schemes and a continuing threat today to the survival of farming in arid lands from Mexico to Australia. Jim Rhoades at the US government's Salinity Laboratory in California says: 'As long as new territories were available, the shifting of irrigated agriculture temporarily solved the problem.' Today, there are fewer new lands to cultivate. According to the UN's Food and Agriculture Organization, as much as half of all irrigation systems around the world today are seriously affected by salinity or related problems of waterlogging. Some 10,000 square kilometres of land are abandoned every year because of salt encroachment.

While only about 15% of the world's fields are irrigated, they contribute more than a third of our food. Rhoades estimates that a tenth of the total land area of the world is so affected by salt that it limits the growth of crops. Salt, he says, threatens the national economies of Argentina, Egypt, India, Iraq, Iran, Pakistan and Syria, where crop losses due to salt in the irrigated fields of the Euphrates valley are currently put at $300 million a year. In India, 35% of all irrigated land is seriously saline. The Murray-Darling basin in south-east Australia provides almost half of that country's agricultural production. By the end of the century, says the New South Wales Department of Agriculture, 'as much as 90% of the irrigated areas in some locations may be affected.'

The salt comes from the natural weathering of rocks by water. Much of it is 'table salt', sodium chloride. When a river is undisturbed, the salt washes to the sea, where it maintains the saltiness of the oceans. But when humans divert river water to irrigate fields they upset the process. Plants absorb the water but leave the salt in the soil. In most of the world's irrigation systems, leaky canals and profligate watering of fields causes the water level in the ground to rise until it brings salt close to the surface. There it kills crops.

If enough water pours on to the land, and then drains away afterwards, it flushes the soil clean. The Nile valley in Egypt has been irrigated continuously for 5,000 years. Until recently, it was free of salt because the Nile flooded the fields each year, washing out the salt. Since the completion upstream of the Aswan dam, the fields are watered by canals rather than floods. Now the levels of salt are rising rapidly.

Amir Muhammed, the chairman of Pakistan's Agriculture Research Council, says: 'Salinity is the number one problem for agriculture in Pakistan.' Four-fifths of the fields in this country of 90 million people are irrigated, mostly with water from the River Indus and its tributaries. Pakistan has one of the largest irrigation networks in the world, conceived and largely built the British, who turned the deserts of Sind and the Punjab into fields for wheat and cotton. The canals are fed by giant dams at Tarbela and Mangla in the upper reaches of the Indus.

The problem is that the British engineers who built the canals left before digging the drainage canals. Virtually none of the water poured on to the fields ever reaches the sea. All its salt, therefore, accumulates on the land, at the rate of two tonnes of salt per irrigated hectare per year. In many parts of the country the fields are covered by a thick white crust of salt. One estimate is that 200 hectares of fields are lost to salt every day. A third of the country's irrigated fields are experiencing severe salt problems.

Pakistani archaeologists are digging up the remains of Mohenjodaro, once a shining city state with 35,000 people which flourished amid irrigated fields on the banks of the Indus 5,000 years ago. They believe the city succumbed to soil salinity before being invaded by marauding Aryans. To prevent modern Pakistan suffering the same fate, the country has raised $600 million from aid agencies to install new drains.

Salt is a terrifying enemy. Warren Hall, when director of the US government's Office of Water Resources Research, put it elegantly in 1973:

Salt problems are particularly insidious. They do not come charging at you with trumpets blowing and battle flags flying, a sight to set stirring the hearts of activists in any century. Rather, they slip in almost unnoticed . . . Time is of no concern, for they are supremely confident of their ultimate victory. History is on their side, as are the laws of physics, and chemistry and biology. They have quietly destroyed, without fuss or fanfare, more civilizations than all of the mighty armies of the world.

Georg Borgstrom, a former professor of food science at Michigan State University, told the magazine *Science News*: 'Close to 65% of all irrigated land [in the world] will be destroyed by salt by the end of the century.' And yet it need not, and probably will not, be so.

A massive reappraisal of the many irrigation systems built round the world in the past three decades is under way. Pakistan, with some of the worst problems, is pioneering solutions. Certainly, things should not have been allowed to get so bad. But, equally, all is not lost. Recent surveys show that, with Pakistan's drainage work roughly half way to completion, the salt is retreating. According to Pakistan's Water and Power Development Authority, 'the extent of soil salinity has declined from 44% to about 28%.'

Washing salt from soils does not always end the problem. In Pakistan the new drain will take salt directly to the sea. But in the US's most intensively used river, the Colorado, field drains connect back to the river which, as a result, becomes more and more salty as the water works its way south towards Mexico and the sea. That is a problem for communities downstream. In the mid-1980s, the American government began to build a $300 million desalting works at Yuma in Arizona. It will allow the very saltiest water to be recycled one more time. But the water will be some of the most expensively produced in the world. During the 1980s, there were plans to drain salt from soils throughout the states of the west that are irrigated by the Colorado. But the huge farming surpluses in the US made most projects unviable.

Scientists, meanwhile, are developing new strains of plants that can tolerate salt, and are devising crop rotations that help to cleanse the soil. They are even finding new uses for brine: it can be a medium for growing algae as cheap biomass; it can be piped to power stations for use as cooling water; there is a scheme to use it as a lubricant in a pipeline transporting coal or potash mined in inland states such as Wyoming to the western coast for export to Japan.

Even salt can be put to good use. But the story of salt is a reminder that, from the dawn of civilization, humans have had the power to create environmental disasters for themselves. The difference today is that many of the new threats are global. If our civilization comes to grief by destroying the ozone layer or triggering a runaway warming or cooling of the atmosphere, there will be no other place to go, and no neighbour ready to thrive from our misfortune. We are finding ways to combat salt by removing it, using it or coping with it. Our response to carbon dioxide may need to be much the same.

DECLINE AND FALL

The last scheduled passenger flight to leave Timbuktu airport set off down the runway in early 1985. The Air Mali plane crashed on take-off, killing all but one of its 53 passengers. Today the only flights to and from Timbuktu are chartered by relief agencies. The roads are a nightmare of dust and potholes, dotted lines on the map. Tarmac never reached Timbuktu. Kabara, the nearby port on the River Niger, is virtually shut off by sand.

A sign welcomes visitors to 'the pearl of the desert', but tourists are becoming rare. The sands of the Sahara are moving south. The grasslands around the city, where Tuareg nomads grazed their cattle, are gone. So too are most of the acacia trees which until recently made Mali one of the world's leading exporters of their sap, gum arabic. Satellite pictures reveal a widening 'noose' of desert around Timbuktu.

Eight hundred years ago, the city was the toast of north Africa, a great centre for both commerce and culture — Paris and New York combined. It was where the Arab and African worlds met, exchanging gold from the forests for salt from the desert. It had two universities and 20,000 students. By the sixteenth century, when Timbuktu was the brightest star in the Songhai empire, more than 100,000 people lived within its walls, making it one of the larger cities in the world. Today, the population is down to 9,000.

The name lives on, of course. A television station found that most Americans had heard of Timbuktu, but did not know where or what it was. Many thought it might be the name of an old musical. But, despite the efforts of an American charity called The Friends of Timbuktu and plans by UNESCO to preserve some ancient buildings, the city seems doomed. Like the stricken plane at the end of its runway, Timbuktu is the victim of a collision between the desert and the modern world.

The image of the advancing desert is a powerful one, and all too real along the southern edge of the Saharan desert — from Mauritania in the west, and the land-locked states such as Mali, Niger and Chad, to Sudan in the east. The name of this desert margin is the Sahel. Since the early 1970s, the word has become a byword for environmental decay and human despair.

Dust storms are one awesome sign of the destructive power of the desert, a clear indication that the desert dunes are on the move. Nicholas Middleton of the University of Oxford has studied dust storms in Mauritania, a vast empty country where the dunes of the Sahara reach the Atlantic Ocean. In the 1960s, the capital, Nouakchott, had five days of storms a year. By the 1980s, they raged on average for 80 days a year. Much of the sand is coming from old 'fossil' dunes that have not moved for 40,000 years. Their reactivation, says Middleton, 'is transforming the region into a large-scale dust exporting zone'.

As fields and pastures disappear and whole villages are buried, the people head for the capital, the only city of any size in this desperately poor country. Before the dust storms began, Nouakchott had 20,000 inhabitants; today 350,000 people live there — half are officially classified as refugees. Today 85% of Mauritania's once nomadic people live in cities.

The dunes are advancing on Nouakchott at a rate of six kilometres a year. In places, they have reached the outskirts. Expanding to meet them are the squatter camps of the city's refugees. In 1960, 120,000 square kilometres of the country were fit for farming or grazing. Today that figure is down to 10,000 square kilometres, less than 1% of the country's land.

Most people make their way to the capital along the Highway of Hope, the country's only proper road. It is 1,100 kilometres long and crosses most of the south of the country. Outside Nouakchott, bulldozers clear fresh sand from the highway each morning. Elsewhere, the road is partly or totally buried for much of its length as dunes march across the landscape. An international mission is attempting to fix Mauritania's dunes by planting trees along their tops. Five of its six projects are dedicated to clearing the road. But at Maghta Lahjar, 400 kilometres east of the capital along the Highway of Hope, the mission has planted a ring of woodland round the town. The result: sand no longer clogs houses and fields. 'The houses were once covered to the roof with sand. Now all the sand has disappeared gradually, just as it had come,' one resident told a visiting journalist in 1986.

For the most part, however, the sands continue to blow. From time to time, the dust storms become caught up with strong air currents that take the grains of dust high into the atmosphere. They can travel for thousands of kilometres before falling to earth, usually in rain. Mauritania is the prime source, says Andrew Goudie from Oxford University, for the increasing fallout of 'red dust' from the Sahara over Europe. There have been seventeen major downpours of desert dust over the British Isles since 1900, ten in the 1980s. 'We are witnessing in Britain the consequences of drought and desertification in Africa,' says Goudie.

In Florida, scientists at the University of Miami have noticed more dust crossing the Atlantic on the trade winds from Africa. It shows up in the air from Miami to north-east Brazil. During the African drought of 1983, ten times more dust reached Barbados than in the late 1960s. The researchers warned in a paper in *Nature* that the dust could influence global weather systems by blocking out sunlight.

RAIN IN THE DESERT

At the heart of the Sahel, straddling the borders between Niger, Nigeria and Chad, is Lake Chad. This inland sea collects the water of two of the region's largest rivers, the Chari and Logone, and drains 2.5 million square kilometres, an area a third the size of the US. Its level is a reliable indicator of the rainfall in a region where a change of a few centimetres over a year can make the difference between life and death, yet where rain gauges of the kind found in thousands of schools throughout the developed world are rare. The fate of the lake over the past quarter century is another graphic indicator of decay in the Sahel.

In past millenniums, the rains of the region made Lake Chad one of the great inland seas of the world. Around 9,000 years ago, after the end of the most recent ice age, the lake's surface was some 40 metres higher than today and the water covered 350,000 square kilometres, making it about the size of the present Caspian Sea. It was a time when elephants, giraffes and antelope ranged over the Sahara. As rainfall has diminished since then, the lake has shrunk, until in 1963 it covered 23,500 square kilometres, an area a little larger than Wales. Then things got serious. By 1973 it had decreased to a third of its size a decade before and it had divided into two parts. By 1985 it had shrunk again to 2,000 square kilometres, less than a tenth its size in 1963. Today, the rotting hulks of fishing boats sit up to 50 kilometres from the present shoreline.

Rainfall in the Sahel reached a modern-day peak in the 1950s, when every year had more rain than the average of recent decades. The 1960s fluctuated, but since 1969 rainfall has been below average every year, reaching new depths of drought in the mid-1980s. It has been the Sahel's most severe and longest drought this century, only partially broken by the rains that brought floods in the summer of 1988. Eugene Rasmusson from the US's Climate Analysis Center says: 'Each succeeding dry episode since the early 1960s has been more extreme than the previous one.' A few dry years have caused famines in the Sahel before. But this sustained decline could, he says, be a long-term trend that requires a radical rethink about how people live in the region.

The story of the drought in the Sahel and Ethiopia is known almost too well. The television-watching masses of the Western world all have a view on what has gone wrong there in the past two decades. The trouble is that much of what they say may be wrong. And in making wrong judge-ments we may be storing up new troubles for future generations on the margins of the deserts. The key question is whether the region's growing despair arises primarily from the meteorological drought or from human misuse of the Sahelian environment.

The *National Geographic* magazine thinks it knows the answer to that question. It began a long cover feature on 'Africa's Stricken Sahel' in August 1987: 'Drought is natural to the Sahel; what is not is the overgrazing and deforestation that have helped the desert overrun an area roughly the size of France and Austria in 50 years.' In fact, the droughts of the 1970s and 1980s were something that the people of the Sahel are palpably not used to.

Derek Winstanley, a British meteorologist who has charted the rains of the Sahel since the 1960s, was the first to warn, in 1973, of the impending meteorological crisis for the region. He believed then that climatic zones, which provide anyone driving just a few hundred kilometres north or south in the Sahel with an abrupt shift from lush greenery to desert, were on the move. He wrote in *Nature* that year that 'in the Sahel, a southward shift of the climatic zones of only one degree of latitude ... means a decrease in rainfall of some 40 to 50%.' He noted that 'from 1960 to 1970 there was an average decrease of 65 millimetres in the mean seasonal rainfall' at a number of rainfall stations in the Sahel, and translated this as a southward march of the desert climate at a rate of nine kilometres a year. The shifts in the atmospheric circulation determining the extent of the desert followed cycles that were identifiable over decades, and he predicted the southward march of the desert would continue until around 2030. By then, the desert would be some 180 kilometres further south than in 1930. His ideas were dismissed by most of his fellows — so much so that he left Britain for the US a disillusioned man.

Fifteen years later, the desert had followed his prediction, but he still won only grudging acceptance for his ideas. The logic of his case is, he says, that much of the work done by the UN and others since the mid-1970s to hold back the Sahara, by planting trees for instance, is doomed to fail.

The consequences of the drying of the Sahel may be horrific, but are they important to the future of the planet?

The answer is that they could be. Nobody knows whether the changes we are inflicting on the atmosphere have influenced the climate of the Sahel. We do not even know whether the greenhouse warming will worsen or alleviate the Sahelian crisis. The one certainty is that, as we change our atmosphere, many more areas will find that their climates and environments are changing suddenly, and often for the worse. The problems of Africa have become the most severe modern test of the world's ability to sustain its people. The issues raised are cultural, political and economic as well as environmental and scientific. They are no easier for having often been faced before in other continents. In the remainder of this chapter we look in more detail at some of those problems. They illustrate the huge range of issues that arise when nations are under economic or environmental stress — not the least among them is establishing exactly what the problem is.

Our inability to disentangle the various possible causes of decline in Africa in general and the Sahel in particular does not bode well for our chances of deciding what to do if, say, the grain belt in the US or the Ukraine dries out. In 1988, as parts of the US suffered their third drought in four years, farmers wondered whether the change in rainfall levels was likely to be permanent. Should they sell up and move north to Canada, or should they wait for better times? Millions more farmers will be asking similar questions in the coming decades. They will need answers.

AFRICA ON THE HOOF

Kebede Tato must have one of the least enviable jobs in the world. He is head of soils and water in Ethiopia's Ministry of Agriculture. When my colleague, Debora MacKenzie, visited that country in summer 1987, Kebede was pondering the state of the Ethiopian highlands, remote provinces such as Wollo and Tigre, whose names had become famous during the famine of three years before. Half the farm soils in the highlands — 140,000 square kilometres, or an area of land slightly larger than England — were 'severely degraded', he said. The highlands lose three billion tonnes of soil a year. Some reports put annual losses on sloping fields at up to 100 tonnes per hectare.

MacKenzie described the scene from above:

> To a European, the land looks upside-down. The farms sit not in valleys but on what look like the flat tops of mountains. The highland plateau is split by eroded chasms, and the greens and browns of crops and pasture stop only where the land falls sharply away into steep gullies of rock and soil. You can almost see the fields crumbling away at the edges. In the chasms, anywhere the slope is less than vertical, more fields cling. At the bottom, the streams are red with soil.

From the harsh images on our television screens it is difficult to imagine that a century ago trees covered 40% of Ethiopia. Now, says Kebede, the figure is down to 3%. Some see the destruction of trees as the start of the decline of the Ethiopian highlands. Trees, with their long roots, are very efficient at bringing to the surface of the soil both water and the minerals that make soils fertile. When the trees are chopped down, the soil dries out and its fertility declines. It is blown away by winds or washed away into rivers whenever it rains.

Farmers chop down trees for firewood. But when the trees are all gone, they take animal dung and the leftovers of crops from the land to burn. In poor countries dung and crop residues are a prime form of fertilizer for soils. In the absence of artificial fertilizers, these organic wastes return to the soil the nutrients taken up by crops. If farmers instead remove dung and crop wastes for fuel, then the soil loses more of its fertility and its structure begins to decay, leaving it loose and crumbly, ready to be taken away by wind and water. The finest particles go first, leaving shallow, coarser soils that hold less water during a growing season. The Ethiopian highlands have always been vulnerable to erosion. Many Sudanese crops grow in Ethiopian silt washed downstream by the Blue Nile. But some experts reckon that in the mid-1980s Wollo was losing 0.5% of its soil every year.

There are many causes of soil erosion. It is difficult to

generalize, but the tilling of land for arable crops almost always encourages erosion. One recent study for the International Association for the Hydrological Sciences estimated that 'soil erosion on a field is on average two orders of magnitude [that is, a hundred times] more than that under a forest and one order of magnitude [ten times] more than from non-forested landscapes.' The study, by Genady Golubev from the Department of Hydrology at Moscow State University, concluded that the worldwide loss of soils from erosion by water alone was currently 90 billion tonnes a year, five times the rate in neolithic times and double that of a century ago. Rates of soil erosion in Africa are in fact much lower than those in Asia. Yet they are just as damaging because the chemical weathering of the continent's ancient rocks is also much slower, so the formation of new soil is slow.

Fields on the dry, sloping margins of cultivatable land are especially vulnerable to erosion. The spread of farming into the Sahel, and especially on to slopes such as those in the Ethiopian highlands, has much to do with the African crisis. The encroachment of farmers also pens the traditional nomadic herders of the dry lands into ever smaller, drier and more inhospitable areas. The wetter lands where they once took their cattle during droughts is now fenced off. Efforts to help them by, for example, digging new waterholes, have often only compounded the problem by encouraging them to increase their herds, which then overgraze the thin grasslands around the waterholes.

The annexation of grazing lands by farmers with ploughs and fences is one of the most important worldwide changes of the past two centuries. The plough has invaded the Great Plains of the US, the southern African veldt, the pampas of South America and the Russian steppes. Ecological crisis has often followed. The Great Plains faced theirs in the 1930s' dust bowl. The Sahel is suffering now.

The nomads of the Sahel get a raw deal. Farmers grab their land. Governments want to tie them down, stop their irritating habit of crossing national borders they barely know exist, and make them pay taxes. Across the highlands of Kenya and Tanzania, the nomads have been thrown off their traditional lands to make way for parks where tourists can hunt big game with cameras.

The tensions between the settled and the nomadic in Africa, rather like those involving gypsies in parts of Europe, have a long history. A fourteenth-century historian, Ibn Khaldun, complained that 'civilization always collapsed in places where the [nomads] took over ... such settlements were depopulated and the very earth there turned into something that was no longer earth.' The UN's Food and Agriculture Organization added the view of the modern state during a study of west Africa's problems, published in 1973. Pastoralists, it said, 'caring for nothing, disdaining manual labour, balking at paying taxes, and being unwilling to sell their animals ... do not make the economic contribution to their countries that is rightfully expected of them'.

The modern view is that there are too many cattle on the grasslands of the Sahel and that overgrazing is turning the land to desert. The journal *Science* cited as 'perhaps the most graphic proof of this' a 'green pentagon' discovered in satellite photographs of the Sahel taken in the early 1970s.

The difference between [the green pentagon] and the surrounding desert was nothing more than a barbed wire fence. Within was a 250,000-acre ranch. The simple protection afforded the land was enough to make the difference between pasture and desert.

Certainly, there are many more cattle in the Sahel today. There are around twice as many animals grazing there as 40 years ago, perhaps 25 million in all, and on rather less land. But the pastoralists have their defenders. As persuasive as the satellite image of the green pentagon is a study of the Borana nomads of southern Ethiopia. The International Livestock Centre for Africa, which is based in Addis Ababa, found the Borana's use of the land to be very productive: 'Compared with Australian commercial ranches in a very similar climatic environment, the Borana produce nearly four times as much protein and six times as much food energy from each hectare.' In 1987, the director of the centre, an Irish dairy farmer called John Walsh, told MacKenzie: 'It is very hard to intervene and change their lifestyle or to increase animal production in that environment without doing ecological damage.'

In Botswana, on the fringes of the Kalahari desert in southern Africa, another study found that pastoralists produced twice as much food on each hectare as ranchers. Michael Horowitz and Peter Little of the Institute for Development Anthropology in the US came up with a trenchant defence of the African pastoralist at a conference on drought and hunger in Africa, held in the aftermath of the drought of 1983. Since the famine of the early 1970s, they said, more than a decade of attempts to bring modern science and modern farming methods to cattle raising in the Sahel had failed to improve productivity or reduce the nomads' vulnerability to drought. The nomads were already doing it right.

It was the settled farmers who were getting it wrong, and who were compensating for the declining productivity of their own land by extending their fences across the nomads' pastures. The spread of government-backed irrigation schemes to grow crops for export, and the demands of towns and cities for firewood were also damaging the Sahel.

In Sudan, the exhaustion of soils has caused yields of millet to fall throughout the country. To make up for this, between 1960 and 1975 the people increased almost threefold the area used to cultivate millet. Fields extended west into Darfur, a remote region which was later hit badly by the drought of 1984.

In Niger, the average grain yield for each hectare fell from 500 kilograms in 1920 to 350 kilograms in 1978. Farmers headed north to find new land to cultivate. Neither the southward march of the desert sands, nor the drought of the early 1970s stopped them. In 1983, French investigators reported, 'we saw an almost unbroken chain of fields along the road from Tahoua to Agadez as far as Abalak, that is some 80 kilometres north of the officially defined limit for rainfed agriculture.'

Governments of the Sahel seem unable or unwilling to prevent the spread of farming into areas where it can only cause ecological chaos. This is partly because of the ambivalence of governments about how much damage the nomads themselves are doing.

A critical question for the future is how resilient the Sahel's grasslands are. How well can they 'bounce back' from decline? The evidence is that the land can recover quickly. Even in the midst of drought, a brief downpour of rain will turn the entire landscape green. But the combination of more cattle and worse drought could have taken the nomads' land 'beyond the point of no return'.

Aid agencies say that African governments should encourage nomads to sell more of their cattle and reduce the number of animals on the land. But Robert Bement, an American rancher who leads a team of ecologists working in Niger for the US Agency for International Development, warns that most pastures are actually underused. 'Contrary to conventional wisdom, moderate grazing in the early rainy season (which, in fact, is the practice of Nigerian pastoralists) provides for greater ... soil moisture than does the lighter grazing pressure more often recommended by pasture management specialists.' Increase the soil moisture and more vegetation grows, allowing more animals to live on the land.

Other studies point out that the kinds of plants growing in the area will evolve according to the use made of the land. More intense grazing may encourage the spread of plants that provide more foliage. This has already happened on the Sahel grasslands, where the short dense grasses allow the cattle to consume more energy per bite. Tall grass looks more lush, but a study of Tanzania's Serengeti National Park, reported in *Science*, found that 'vegetation taller than 40 centimetres' contained too little usable nutrients to allow a cow to survive. Green pentagons seen from space may look productive, but appearances can be deceptive — especially in the Sahel.

The world of the Sahelian nomads may well be disappearing. It is difficult to see how, in the long run, they can maintain their current way of life. They face the same fate as the American Indians of the Great Plains, the Zulus of southern Africa and the Tartars who, under Genghis Khan, controlled a huge domain across central Asia and west into Europe in the thirteenth century. But the pressures that will defeat them are political and economic, not environmental. As Horowitz and Little put it: 'Africa's arid and semi-arid

zones are mainly suited to extensive livestock production.'
The real ecological damage at present is being done by the
sedentary farmers.

African farming is an enigma. The continent is vast and
only thinly populated. The UN's Food and Agriculture
Organization says that, with current methods of farming,
Africa could provide food for several times its existing
population. And yet, from Mozambique to Mauritania, the
continent appears to have lost the ability to feed itself. In
1984, 140 million of its 531 million people relied on grain
from outside the continent. Between the mid-1970s and the
mid-1980s, food production per head declined by more than
10%. Twenty years ago, both Ethiopia and Sudan were
hailed as having the potential to become the 'breadbasket of
Africa'. Few would claim that today and yet it could still be
true. What is needed is the kind of 'green revolution' which
transformed farming throughout Asia two decades ago.

Rattan Lal, a soil scientist working for the International
Institute of Tropical Agriculture in Ibadan, Nigeria, is one
of the people trying to bring that transformation about. He
says:

Much of the agrarian stagnation in Africa is caused by
neglect and misuse of the most basic of resources, soil. In
fact the root cause of the perpetual famine can be traced
to the misuse of soil and water resources ... Substantial increases in food production are possible if the proven technologies can be effectively transferred and implemented.

Three decades ago, India was racked by famine. Two
decades ago, Bangladesh was described as the 'basket case
of the world'. Yet, despite soaring populations, both countries appear now to be free of famine. A severe drought in
much of India in the mid-1980s, culminating in doom-laden
headlines round the world in 1987, did not bring India to the
brink of famine, because the country had spare grain in silos
everywhere from the Punjab to Bengal.

Both India and Bangladesh have shared in the huge

increase in rice yields throughout Asia. Modern hybrids developed at the International Rice Research Centre in the Philippines have helped raise average yields of 1.2 tonnes per hectare in 1960 to 3.2 tonnes by 1985. Many Bangladeshi farmers now grow a wheat crop between their two traditional rice crops. New strains have tripled wheat yields in Bangladesh and the country's annual production has grown fifteenfold since 1960 to some 1.5 million tonnes today.

A generation ago, there were half as many people on the planet as today and, as famines raged in Asia, few believed that the world could continue to feed itself. Yet through the 1980s world food stocks have soared. A ministerial meeting of the World Food Council, in Beijing in June 1987, heard that world cereal stocks were at record levels, and prices for food on the world market were at their lowest since the 1930s.

Many people believe that the food glut is largely the result of soaring yields in the developed nations. Not so. Between the mid-1970s and mid-1980s, farm output rose by 1.6% each year in the developed countries, but by 3.8% each year in the less developed nations. North America and Europe are left with grain mountains because poor nations to which they once sold, such as India, Indonesia, Brazil and Thailand, have become exporters themselves.

Most of this revolution has passed Africa by. New Asian crops do not grow well in African fields. So countries with some of the fastest population growth rates, and some of the most vulnerable natural environments, are left without the tools to face the future. Lal estimated in 1987 that only 6.5% of the fields of Africa were planted with new high-yielding crop varieties, the products of the green revolution. This is partly because scientists have not yet developed the varieties, and partly because the countries are too poor to provide the irrigation and buy the fertilizers these crops need.

Now Lal's research centre and another at the International Center for Research in the Semi-Arid Tropics (ICRISAT) in Mali are coming to the rescue. They are breeding better strains of millet and sorghum, the main grain crops of dry lands in Africa, and developing grains such as chickpeas and pigeonpeas which can enrich soils by 'fixing' nitrogen from the air.

A new hybrid of sorghum from ICRISAT tested in Zimbabwe is apparently so resistant to drought that it can yield more grain in a bad year than local varieties do in a good year. An even tougher variety promises to do the same for the Sahel. Lal's centre in Nigeria is breeding varieties of other African staple crops, such as cassava, which resist pests such as the green spider mite and the cassava mealybug.

Other researchers are finding ways to cultivate the vast areas of untilled soils that make a mockery of Africa's hardships. These include the heavy jet-black vertisols that cover much of the Nile valley in Sudan, the huge basin around Lake Chad in the central Sahel and, not least, Ethiopia. Vertisols feel like modelling clay and easily become waterlogged. In the dry Ethiopian highlands their capacity to hold water could be a godsend if the soils could be drained. Ethiopia has 130,000 square kilometres of vertisols, of which less than a sixth is farmed. The search is on to find a simple plough that can drain the soils.

One day, biotechnology will add the 'gene revolution' to the green revolution. Scientists will transfer genes from one plant to another. The holy grail for this work, at any rate in Africa, is the transfer of the nitrogen-fixing gene from *légumes* such as peas and beans to standard grains. This could end for ever the reliance of farmers on expensive nitrogen fertilizers. A more immediate prospect is a sorghum which contains the gene that produces the gluten protein. Sorghum is the most drought-resistant of all grains. But most people, given the choice, prefer wheat to sorghum because gluten makes it taste better. Splicing the gluten gene to sorghum would change that.

Yields on many farms would increase if farmers threw away their tractors and brought back oxen, which do not compact the soil. Digging terraces and embankments of various sorts on the sloping fields of the Ethiopian highlands and elsewhere would frequently halt soil erosion.

Spectacular gains in crop yields are flowing from 'agroforestry', the revival of the practice of planting trees alongside crops. The wood and fallen leaves of trees return to the soil the nutrients lost when ancient forests were cut down, and reduce soil erosion. Some trees, such as the *leucaena*, also fix nitrogen. The *leucaena* is credited with reclaiming large tracts of useless land in India and south-east Asia and is now being tried in Africa. Farm animals will also eat the leaves and provide manure. Lal believes that 'integrating livestock raising with tree crops and food crops is an important link in providing the needed diversity for an ecologically sustainable [farming] system.'

Better yields also follow if soils are ploughed regularly. And, in many places, simple irrigation systems in which villagers harvest local water rather than taking supplies from vast dams have great potential in a continent where, outside Egypt, irrigation has never caught on. Lal says that 'insufficient water supply is the most important single factor governing soil productivity.'

Most of these initiatives require a lot of work but very little money. Africa is often called over-populated because it cannot feed its people. Yet many places are chronically short of labour to tend the fields. Lal points out: 'At present, high populations are a definite liability and a major cause of food shortages. [But] human resources, if trained and used properly, can be a major asset.' Africa has unrivalled potential to produce more food. This is just as well since it probably also has an unparalleled population explosion ahead.

Leaving aside the land that could be farmed using irrigation, Africa has some 800 million hectares of good cropland, only a fifth of which is currently cultivated. The cropland is not always close to the people who need it. But among the seven countries with the greatest potential to produce more food than they eat are two that have suffered worst from famine in the 1980s: Sudan and Mozambique.

The problems for farming in Africa are immense. But the doom-mongers who predict that Africa will turn into some hell on Earth are doing Africans a disservice. Provided that nobody writes the continent off, Africa can find its way into the twenty-first century, just as, in their different ways, China, 'the land of famine' in the 1930s, and the desperate India of the 1950s and 1960s have prospered.

4

LIFE AND DEATH OF THE RAINFORESTS

THE WOODCHOPPERS' BALL

Many Europeans still think the 'dark continent' of Africa is jungle. But, from the humid equator to the parched lands of the Sahel and the highlands of East Africa, the past century has seen a staggering destruction of forests. Lester Brown, the director of the Worldwatch Institute in Washington, says that 'the destruction of tree cover in Africa represents one of the most dramatic human alterations of the environment on record.' Settlers have cut down trees for firewood, for logs to export to Europe and North America, and to make way for mines and fields.

West African records suggest that the Ivory Coast has lost 70% of its forests this century, Ghana 64% and Liberia 69%. As much as two-thirds of West Africa's former forests may have disappeared. The rate of destruction in the mid-1980s, according to the UN's Food and Agriculture Organization, was around 5% per year.

The story of Sierra Leone, pieced together by Vivien Gornitz from Columbia University in the US, is typical:

Most of Sierra Leone was formerly covered by ever-green and semi-deciduous forest ... The widespread deforestation began with the settlement of Freetown [the capital] and environs in the early nineteenth century. Logging for teak and other hardwoods began along the

72

rivers of the northern Sierra Leone, and expanded south-
wards by the 1840s.

Oil palms invaded the original forest, he says, though the
interior of the country remained largely forested until early
in this century.

But by 1947, the mountains were bare and the plains were
largely grassland with only patches of secondary thickets.
Around 1900, the area between Songo and Moyamba was
still forested; by 1920 it had been reduced to low scrub . . .
Coastal mangroves have been cleared for rice production.
Clearing intensified after the 1930s, partly to compensate
for the severe soil erosion in upland rice areas.

Nobody is sure how extensive tropical forests once were.
One widely accepted estimate is that they covered 25 million
square kilometres, 16% of the land surface of the planet.
Today, they cover around ten million cubic kilometres. Half
of the loss has been to permanent farms, another quarter to
pastures and the final quarter is, at any one time, under
shifting cultivation. The impact of shifting cultivators on the
forests is one of the most controversial and difficult to
estimate. As we shall see later, the debate has implications
both for estimates of the rate of loss of tropical forests today,
and for the role of deforestation in the greenhouse effect and
the wider crisis of the chemistry of the atmosphere.

Shifting cultivators round the world have for millenniums
been farming the forests. It probably started with the
discovery of fire. Farmers soon began to burn clearings in
forests. The ash fertilized soils and provided a good crop for
a few years until the soil was exhausted. Then the cultivators
moved on. Usually the forest returned. Gornitz believes that
few of the forests being cut down in West Africa are virgin
forests. Most are regrowth, following the path of shifting
cultivators.

On the drier fringes of the tropical forests, these primitive
farmers, often pejoratively known as 'slashers and burners',
left a permanent mark. Gornitz reports that in Cameroon
'much of the original forest between 4 and 6°N has been

73

replaced by a tree or shrub savannah, over centuries of shifting cultivation.' Perhaps 40% of Africa's ancient equatorial forests had been converted to savannah grasslands over the millenniums before the past century of destruction began.

Similar figures may hold for Indonesia and South America. Some investigators believe that almost all the savannah grasslands bordering tropical rainforests were created by shifting cultivators. If this is true, it has had an extraordinary and so far largely unacknowledged human impact on the planet. Savannah lands today cover fifteen million square kilometres, roughly 10% of the land surface of the planet. As we shall see later, there is good evidence that changes to natural vegetation on this scale could have influenced climates locally and perhaps globally.

A thousand years ago, 80% of central Europe was forested. Today the figure is around 20%. Go back 10,000 years and the whole of the Mediterranean region was covered with oak forests. Five thousand years ago the forests of the Lebanon provided massive supplies of timber for the Phoenician empire. Britain experienced a wood crisis in the sixteenth century because so many trees had been cut down to build ships. The crisis forced the country to turn to coal for burning.

For most of this century, however, the countries of Europe have been planting new trees in intensively managed plantations. In Asia, the Indonesians, Filipinos and Malaysians have butchered their forests, and the naked slopes of the Himalayas now suffer massive soil erosion. But other countries are planting fast. Foremost are South Korea and China, which have planted tens of millions of hectares in the past two decades. The Chinese say they are creating a 'green wall of China'. Despite all that humans have done, a fifth of the world's land surface is still covered by forests. More than half of the total is in the temperate lands away from the tropics.

Roger Sedjo and Marion Clawson from the American research organization Resources for the Future have taken a stand against the apocalyptic predictions for the future of forests. They point out that most of the damage to tropical forests does not take place in the dense virgin forests, the areas of greatest genetic diversity, at all. The great jungles of the Amazon and the Congo basins are more or less undisturbed, with deforestation rates of perhaps 3% per decade. The real destruction is taking place in areas that have been chopped down many times before. In countries such as the Philippines, the traditional shifting cultivators are being squeezed out by the landless poor and rapacious logging companies with their eyes on international markets such as Japan.

Sedjo and Clawson believe that away from the virgin heartlands, the tropical forests will eventually develop into managed commercial reserves in much the same way as the temperate forests have. 'Forestry today is experiencing a transition similar to that experienced two or three millennia ago in agriculture,' they say. 'Just as agriculture evolved from gathering and hunting to cropping and livestock raising, similarly forestry is beginning to evolve from the gathering of natural inventories to the cropping of forest plantations.' This may turn out to be so. But from the Amazon rainforest, it is difficult to spot the transition.

LURE OF THE AMAZON

The Amazon basin has seen false economic dawns before. Its only large town, Manaus, was known 80 years ago as the 'Paris of the Tropics'. Built from the profits of a booming trade in rubber, the town boasted an opera house, the Teatro Amazonas, which was copied from La Scala in Milan and, so the story goes, the town's high society sent its laundry to Portugal. Then Malaya cornered the market in rubber and boom turned to bust. The forests that cover the basin moved in on the town. Today, the lure of the Amazon, one of the last great wildernesses on Earth, has taken hold again. For both the landless poor of São Paulo and the world's richest, it is a chance to make a fortune.

The Amazon basin is an extraordinary global resource. It contains roughly two-thirds of the world's surviving tropical rainforests, representing some 30% of all the biological material on the land. The tributaries of the River Amazon contain a quarter of the fresh water that is not locked up in ice caps. The discharge to the Atlantic Ocean is five times that of the River Congo, and eleven times that of the Mississippi. The water provides a vast potential source of hydroelectric power which the Brazilian government wants to tap. The basin covers some six million square kilometres, draining more than a third of South America. Beneath it, according to some estimates, lies enough iron ore to last the world for four centuries. In the late 1980s, prospectors found major oil and gas reserves in the lower basin. Water behind the world's fourth largest dam, the Tucurui on the River Tocantins, has flooded 2,000 square kilometres of forest and is driving turbines to fuel giant smelters converting bauxite deposits at Belem and Carajas into aluminium.

The Amazon basin is a wild land, where gangs of thugs hired by landowners throw poor farmers off their land and out of their homes, and where surviving tribes of Indians are liable to find fences hundreds of kilometres long appearing suddenly across their land. The government completed the 4,500-kilometre Trans-Amazon Highway in 1973. The second great road, Route 364, is the 1,500-kilometre 'gateway to the western frontier'. Completed in 1984, it is creating boom towns such as Rolim de Moura which has grown in a decade from a community of four houses to one of 10,000 homes.

There are two common views about these latest attempts to colonize the Amazon basin. The first is that it will all end in tears. It certainly did for Daniel Ludwig, an American shipping magnate. In 1982, he pulled out of a vast development based on a giant pulp mill on the Jari River, where he had planted 200 hectares of trees and built townships for thousands of people, served by 4,500 kilometres of roads.

The second view is that the miners and ranchers will win this time, make their fortunes, chop down the forests, destroy the soils, upset the climate and leave behind a vast wasteland fit only for mining companies. A few optimists claim that much of the Amazon basin can be claimed for permanent cultivation and for the development of industries and cities without destroying it.

Since the completion of Route 364, migrant farmers and cattle ranchers have laid waste tracts of forest in the south

76

and west of Brazil, in the states of Rondonia, Acre and Mato Grosso. Satellite photographs suggest that, between 1982 and 1985, the amount of land bare of trees in Rondonia grew from 10,000 square kilometres to 27,000 square kilometres, 11% of the state. More recent pictures taken during the dry season in 1987 for the Brazilian government's Amazon Research Institute, revealed some 250 fires burning every night along Route 364 in Rondonia, as migrants cleared land for themselves in the jungle. One journalist who visited western Brazil that year reported 'a thin pall of smoke obscuring the sun, fed by thousands of man-made forest fires'. Local airports often close during the dry season because the smoke makes taking off and landing unsafe.

In Mato Grosso (the name means thick forest), some 7% of the state is bare of trees, mostly cut down by cattle ranchers. Whereas peasant farmers clear small patches of forest, ranchers create openings of up to 100 square kilometres at a time. The destruction in these areas is extensive. But it should be kept in proportion. The idea that the Amazon rainforest could disappear within a decade or so is nonsense. Away from the new roads, the forests are, for the moment, untouched. The overall rate of destruction of Brazilian forests is less than 1% a year. And that takes no account of any new planting and regrowth of forest.

Regrowth may be extensive. Satellite photographs show that in some places ranchers have abandoned their land after destroying its fertility. Environmentalists had predicted that the forest would not regrow. But the photographs suggest that, in fact, the forest is returning. This seems to be the pattern. In Guatemala, the ancient Mayan civilization levelled huge areas of forest. Yet today the Mayan pyramids are surrounded by thick forest.

A prevalent myth is that tropical rainforests such as the Amazon forests are some ancient phenomenon of the planet. To emphasize this idea, some people call them the planet's 'lung'. The truth is rather different. Fire, for instance, is no newcomer to the forest. Excavation of soils has revealed thick layers of soot which clearly date from before the arrival of humans here. Fire may be part of the natural cycle of life in even the wettest, most remote parts of the forest. Also, we do not have to go back far to find a time when very little of the forest was there at all. An American researcher, Barbara Leyden of the University of Florida, has studied the lush Guatemalan forests. She found that they were, just 10,000 years ago, a dry cool land of scrub and grass. The journal *Science*, reporting her work, concluded that 'tropical forests are dynamic and ephemeral, rather than stable and ancient.' That does not necessarily make it safe to chop down the forest, as we shall see. But at least we know that the planet has done without it before.

The conventional view is that if humans chopped down the forest, it would not regrow. The evidence for that idea seems, on inspection, to be remarkably thin. Another conventional idea is that once the trees are gone, the soils will be useless. That too may be a myth.

FARMING THE FORESTS

Two Brazilian scientists, Peter Vose and Eneas Salati, from the Amazon Research Institute at Manaus, have investigated the impact of cultivation on Amazonian soils. They found that, away from the forest margins, traditional 'slash and burn' farming is rarely harmful. Most of the nutrients in tropical forests are held in the trees themselves and in the mass of fallen litter on the forest floor. The soils themselves are usually thin. When shifting cultivators burn trees, most of the nutrients stay in the ashes, which are spread on the forest floor. As we have seen, this ensures excellent crops for two or three years. After that, provided the farmers move on, the soils should recover within ten or twenty years, they say. One force for recovery may be the spread of nutrients around the forest in fine 'aerosols' of chemicals, which fall back to Earth in rainfall.

When ranchers clear huge areas of forest for cattle pastures (usually to provide the meat for Big Macs in the US), the story is different. Salati and Vose give as an example an area of ranchland in Paragominas in the Para region of Brazil, near the mouth of the Amazon. 'This area was extensively cleared for pasture ... and typically did not receive any fertilizer ... There are now approximately 500,000 hectares that are substantially degraded, and severe erosion [of soils] is extensive.'

Few soils, however good, will go on providing crops forever unless they are treated to replace lost nutrients, or left fallow while nature replenishes them. The key question for the future of the Amazon basin is whether soils that are stripped of trees can be turned successfully to the plough. The answer, surprisingly, seems to be that they can.

Pedro Sanchez from the Department of Soil Science at the North Carolina State University in the US says: 'Technology has been developed which permits continuous production of annual crops in some of the acid infertile soils of the Amazon basin.' At the risk of leaving environmentalists incredulous, he claimed in a long review article in *Science* that 'soil properties are improved with continuous cultivation.'

Sanchez had spent almost a decade following the fate of 21 crops of rice, corn and soya beans harvested over eight years on an experimental field in the Peruvian town of Yurimagaus, the westernmost river port of the Amazon, in the foothills of the Andes. The acid soils there, known as ultisols, are short of phosphorus, potassium and other nutrients, and awash with toxic aluminium. They are, he said, 'typical of much of Amazonia'. Yet, with the right fertilizers, local shifting cultivators found they could farm these acid soils continuously with no decline in yield. The farmers' method of clearing land by slash and burn 'proved superior to modern bull-dozers which compress soils and rip off topsoil'. Sanchez cleared the test field in 1972. 'Without fertilization, yields dropped to zero after the third consecutive crop,' he says. But with fertilization, yields stayed high.

Sanchez was in no doubt about the significance of his findings. He began his paper:

> The humid tropics, which cover about 10% of the world's land surface, is a crucial ecosystem because of its agri-cultural potential and the possible ecological consequences of its deforestation ... [these regions] are blessed with temperatures, rainfall and topography which favour agri-cultural development. The main factors limiting such development are low soil fertility ... and lack of appro-priate soil management technology.

His finding that, correctly managed, these soils could be farmed flew in the face of the conventional wisdom of soil scientists and environmentalists. Many believe that, without trees, the soils of the Amazon basin are useless and doomed to a fate similar to those in the Sahel. (One paper arguing this case bears the lurid title, 'Amazon Jungle: Green Hell to Red Desert?')

Sanchez points out that most of the soils in the Amazon basin are strikingly similar to those of the south-eastern states of the US. He believes that some two million square kilometres of the Amazon basin, the amount covered by flat land made up of well-drained red and yellow utisols and oxisols, could be farmed permanently using his system.

His is a bold vision, of large areas of the basin covered with rice paddies, corn fields and rolling pastures. 'Although shifting cultivation in its traditional form is ecologically sound,' he says, 'it is a guarantee of perpetual poverty for those who practise it.' Without change, farmers may return to soils too soon, causing a spiral of decline of the kind that has overtaken other tropical rainforests from central America to west Africa and the Far East. 'For every hectare that is cleared and put into [permanent cultivation], many hectares of forest may be spared from the axe.' Three crops a year ensure that the soil is protected from erosion by torrential rains.

Even the economics work out. The experimental farm at Yurimagaus is 1,000 kilometres from Lima, the Peruvian capital. All the fertilizers for Sanchez's project had to be bought and carried from Lima. Sanchez reckons, nonetheless, that his methods increased fourfold the income of his shifting cultivators.

It is dangerous to conclude too much from one study, however successful. Perhaps pests will invade Sanchez's fields and destroy the crops. There must be a considerable risk that what may work for one farm could cause ecological havoc if practised widely. But the study demonstrates that a positive approach has a place in the Amazon, and it hints at the extraordinary potential there may still be for expanding peasant agricultural production around the world, sometimes in the most unlikely places. The problem is that agricultural success in the tropical forests could carry the seeds of its own destruction. The loss of trees can affect many things besides soils.

LOSE THE FOREST AND YOU LOSE THE RAIN

The biography of Christopher Columbus, written by his son Ferdinand, describes a journey in the Caribbean in 1494.

> He departed for Jamaica . . . The sky, air and climate were just the same as in other places; every afternoon there was a rain squall that lasted for about an hour. He attributed this to the great forests of that land; he knew from experience that formerly this also occurred in the Canary, Madeira, and Azore Islands, but since the removal of forests that once covered those islands they do not have so much mist and rain as before.

Many people believe that the lands around the Mediterranean have also grown drier since the loss of their trees. But the process is not universal. The loss of the forests that covered Europe has had no discernible effect on rainfall. American pioneers cleared huge tracts of forest without turning the New World into a desert. Since most climatologists come from these cooler climes, the wisdom of Columbus was largely lost to modern science until the 1970s.

It was Jule Charney of the Massachusetts Institute of Technology who revived the idea that vegetation influences weather when he proposed, in 1975, that changing reflectivity of the land surface might have altered the climate in West Africa. Any satellite photograph of the Earth shows deserts as light, reflective surfaces. On the ground, we see this as glare. Sand will reflect up to 50% of the Sun's light directly back into space. Plants are much darker and absorb more heat. So the air above tropical deserts is typically colder than the air above tropical forests.

Charney's idea caught on. In 1979 Carl Sagan from Cornell University suggested that changing reflectivity could have been altering climates ever since humans began to burn down forests. 'Humans have made substantial contributions to global climate changes during the past several millennia,' he said, 'and perhaps over the past million years.' We could have lowered the planet's temperature by about 1°C, he said.

The effect of changing reflectivity on rainfall, however, is difficult to demonstrate in practice. And the changes in the reflectivity of the land caused by man turn out to be rather smaller than Charney and Sagan suggested. Vivien Gornitz examined data from satellites passing over West Africa, an area where the destruction of forests and the spread of deserts has been as extreme as anywhere in the world. He concluded that 'the change in [reflectivity] is relatively small.' Even assuming that the entire Sahel has turned to desert, the average amount of sunlight reflected would not have increased by as much as 4%. This 'represents an upper limit'. In practice, he said, desertification in the Sahel is sporadic and localized, concentrated around towns and boreholes.

There are a number of other theories about possible ways that changes in vegetation on land could change the weather. For instance, deserts increase the amount of dust in the atmosphere. The dust will absorb the Sun's heat, damping down the formation of rainclouds. This process could perpetuate a drought, especially in sandy areas, such as Mauritania, the current dust-storm capital of the world. It is plausible, but nobody knows if it works like that.

Most scientists now believe that the prime human influence on local climates probably involves the complex cycling of water in the vegetation, soils and air of the tropics. The strongest evidence comes, as it did in Columbus's day, from rainforests. Above the Amazon forest, NASA and the Brazilian National Institute for Space Research spent the late 1980s measuring the 'forest's breath' to find out what might happen as the forests are cut down. The first results were published in February 1988, just as record rains caused floods and mudslides which killed more than 300 people to the south in Rio de Janeiro. Despite local suspicion, it is unlikely that tree-felling in the Amazon could have affected climate in Rio. But the 40,000 people left homeless when tributaries of the River Amazon overflowed in Acre, near

Brazil's borders with Peru and Bolivia, probably did have cause to blame tree-felling.

Luiz Molion, a Brazilian atmospheric physicist, told the press that 'major deforestation in the Amazon means more water flowing into the Amazon itself during the rains.' He explained that forest soils can store water taken up during the wet season and supply it to trees in the weeks when it does not rain. Tree roots provide the vital conduits through the soil that allow this reservoir to be tapped. Take away the trees and the mechanism fails. Rainfall does not percolate deep into the soils. Instead it runs off quickly into rivers. The high water levels in the Amazon in February 1988 were, Molion believed, a result of the destruction of trees. The high waters in the main river, he said, 'acted as a natural dam against the water from the tributaries, causing them to flow over, flooding the whole region'.

Soils are not the whole story, however, according to the man who knows most about the hydrology of the Amazon basin. Eneas Salati, the former head of Brazil's Amazon Research Institute at Manaus in the heart of the Amazon jungle, agrees with Columbus. Clouds 'seem to arise almost from the forests'. Seen from space, the wide rivers of the Amazon basin stand out as cloudless, next to the shrouded forests. 'Even on commercial airline flights, it is possible to see that the cumulus cloud sometimes arises from the very top of the forest and that, where the forest thins out as a result of development, there is less cloud,' says Salati.

The Amazon rainforest is a massive water machine. It stores water in soils, the air and trees themselves. Salati fears that even modest destruction of the trees could destabilize that system and set in motion changes to climate which would cripple the delicate life-support systems of the entire forest. The first sign would be less rain over the forest and in the surrounding regions. There would also be a longer dry season and a colder winter.

Such relatively minor changes could have a devastating effect on the Brazilian economy. For many years, winter frosts in southern Brazil have sent commodity brokers round the world into a frenzy. The prospect of the loss of the Brazilian crop sends the price of coffee futures soaring.

Salati believes such frosts could happen more often. Within a decade or so it could be impossible to grow coffee, sugar, oranges, bananas or many of the current profit-makers of the prosperous agricultural region round São Paulo in southern Brazil.

The key to the water machine of the Amazon rainforest is the 12,000 cubic kilometres of rain that falls each year over the Amazon basin. Only half that water, Salati calculates, reaches the vast river system that feeds the River Amazon. The rest is released from rain-soaked leaves right back into the air. Sunlight evaporates some water directly from leaves. The trees absorb the rest for use in photosynthesis and then return it to the air via the leaves, a process known as transpiration. The two processes together are called 'evapotranspiration'. They allow a rapid cycling of water through the forest and keep the forest wet. Once in the air, the water can form clouds and fall again as rain. Remove the trees and there is no evapotranspiration. The water falls only once. Moreover it falls on soils less able to absorb water. That way you create the paradox of more floods and more drought. It floods during the wet season, because more of the rainfall from storms passes into the rivers. And yet there is less rainfall because less water is recycled from the forest to the air.

Small clearings in forests have little effect on either soils or rainfall. But a rash of larger clearings, such as those now appearing in west Brazil, could trigger sudden and major effects. Trees will recolonize individual clearings. But if there are too many clearings close together, the air and soils will both begin to dry out. Once under way, such a process will feed on itself until the trees are all gone. Salati has a doomsday scenario for the Amazon rainforest. He published it in *Science* and it works like this:

Widespread deforestation sets in motion a chain of events. There is an immediate increased surface runoff, such water is lost rapidly to the rivers and ocean, without the possibility of its recharging the soil system and of its recycling through transpiration and precipitation. Evapotranspiration will continue at a high although reduced rate, returning moisture to the atmosphere, but it is drawing from a decreased soil water store. Therefore, ultimately there will be a reduction in the amount of water recycled to the atmosphere and hence diminished local cloud cover, and diminished precipitation, with the net effect that there will be less total water in the system and an increase in solar radiation.

Ann Henderson-Sellers, a British geographer now working in Australia, calculates that these processes could cause an average loss of rainfall across the Amazon basin of 60 centimetres a year, a reduction of about a third. This would be disastrous even in Manuas, at the heart of the basin. There, says Salati, the present short dry season 'is already the maximum that the ecosystem can withstand, and any lengthening of the dry period ... would induce irreversible damages'. One early consequence would be raging forest fires.

In 1982, Yale Mintz from NASA's Goddard Institute conducted an interesting experiment on a computer model of the planet's climate. The model contains data on the day-to-day rates of evapotranspiration around the globe. He replaced this data with two new sets. The first assumed that the entire land surface of the globe was covered in vegetation growing on moist soil, and hence had high rates of evapotranspiration. The second assumed dry barren soils and no evapotranspiration at all.

Mintz and a colleague asked the computer to predict the effects of these two extreme conditions on rainfall. It replied that, with wet soils, rainfall was uniformly high, at between three and six millimetres a day on most continents. With dry soils, rainfall almost ceased in Europe and much of Asia. It continued to rain only in the monsoon areas of India and south-east Asia where moisture for rain comes directly from the oceans. In North America rainfall was less than one millimetre a day in most places. The computer also predicted major changes in the pattern of high and low pressure zones round the globe, which would have triggered further big alterations in weather systems. It was of course an extreme case. But the finding suggests the power that evapotranspiration has over the world's climate — and hence the influence that humans can have when we tinker with the natural vegetation.

Could the destruction of west African forests have caused the drying of the Sahel? Kenneth Hare, Canada's top climatologist, believes it has. In a report for the World Meteorological Organization he wrote:

> In the region of the Sahel that is worst affected by drought ... the initial source of rainfall is the south-west monsoon blowing in across the Guinea coast. Far inland, however, the rain that falls will very probably already have been precipitated once or more, and re-evaporated. If the water-holding capacity of the soil is reduced, there will be increased resistance to such re-evaporation and a decreased reservoir from which to draw it. Removal of deep-rooted shrubs and trees also decreases the opportunity for transpiration.

Studies by Britain's Meteorological Office, by Mintz at NASA and by others all suggest that the amount of moisture in soils at the beginning of a rainy season is a good predictor of how much rain will fall during that season. If the soil is wet at the start of the rainy season, the weather could still be dry — that depends on whether the atmospheric circulation brings conditions that allow rainfall. But, says Mintz, 'if the soil is dry so that there is little or no evapotranspiration to keep the atmosphere moist, the [coming season] will have little rainfall.'

Sagan may yet be proved right in claiming that we have been influencing climate for many millenniums without ever realizing it. The pace of change in the modern world makes it imperative that we find out for certain.

5

BUGS ON CLOUD NINE

A FUTURE IN TEA LEAVES

The tea plantations of Kericho in western Kenya have an odd claim to fame. Hail falls there on an average of 132 days each year, which is probably a world record. Russell Schnell from the University of Colorado in the US has investigated why there is so much hail there. He believes that 'the feet of hundreds of tea pickers going about their daily jobs' are partly to blame.

How come? It all has to do with clouds. The physics and chemistry of the formation of clouds are horrendously complicated and badly understood. It now seems that biology is involved too. Precipitation, whether rain, snow or hail, forms in clouds when tiny foreign particles act as nuclei around which water droplets or ice crystals can form. Some particles are much better than others at this. While investigating hail in Kericho, Schnell discovered that tiny particles of dead and decaying leaves, which collected on the soil of the local tea plantations, bore a marked resemblance to particles at the heart of local hailstones. Schnell also collected organic litter from nearby forests. Laboratory experiments revealed that both sets of organic particles were far superior to ordinary dust at forming hailstones, but that the tiny fragments of old tea plants were many times better than the forest litter. The feet of the tea pickers, Schnell surmised, had inadvertently been kicking these fragments into the air, turning into a record-breaker an already wondrously efficient natural system for creating clouds to keep plants watered.

This little-noticed study was published in 1982 in *Tellus*, the small journal that published Lovelock's earliest papers on Gaia. It was important evidence for a very Gaian suspicion that bacteria and other organic material from both land and sea are highly efficient at creating clouds.

Much of Schnell's work in this field has been with a bacterium known as *Pseudomonas syringae*. A single gram of the bodies of these bacteria can produce up to a million nuclei for the formation of ice crystals. This knack helps the bacteria with their prime task of helping leaves to rot. When leaves fall, the bacteria on the floor of forests attach themselves to the leaves. On the surface of a leaf, the organisms can help frost to form. Frost damages the tissue of many plants, rupturing cells. The bacteria feed on the contents of these damaged cells and proliferate, speeding up the process of decay and fertilization of soils. Interestingly, says Schnell, the bacteria appear to 'turn on' their ice nucleating ability as temperatures fall. The process has now been seen at work on fourteen different species of trees from as far apart as the Soviet Union, Japan and the Bahamas.

Now it seems that the bacteria have a second job — in the clouds. Schnell says that 'these unique bacteria have evolved a method to both increase the rainfall for plants they live on, and to then preferentially harvest these plants and exploit the resulting food source.'

The findings are dramatically altering the conventional view about clouds, which turn out to be vibrant living environments, rather like soils. Some micro-organisms may spend their entire lives within what Schnell calls 'the humid, nutrient-rich confines of some cloud systems'. Their entire purpose in life, it seems, is to create rain to help other organisms on the ground to grow.

This is all grist to the Gaian mill. But it also offers another potentially potent way in which the destruction of vegetation, by farmers or drought, could trigger more drought and devastation among plants. Schnell proposed as long ago as 1975 that 'massive overgrazing in the Sahel (which preceded the recent drought) resulted in removal of local biogenic ice nuclei and a subsequent reduction in precipitation.' He backed the hypothesis with data collected from Niger in the

Sahel during the drought summer of 1974. This showed many more ice nuclei in decaying vegetation than in soils.

Until the 1970s, nobody believed that ice crystals could form in clouds in the tropics. It was too warm. They assumed that rainfall was created by an alternative process in which individual water droplets coalesce until they grow large enough to fall to the ground. It now seems that much of the rain over the Sahel could start with ice nuclei, and that, from all the data collected by Schnell, suggests a place at centre stage for bacteria that feed on rotting plants. Without the plants, and hence without the bacteria, rainfall could diminish.

One alarming sidelight is that genetic engineers have taken a strong interest in *Pseudomonas syringae*. They want to find ways of neutralizing its ability to create frost damage on sensitive and valuable crops, such as strawberries. The work was being pioneered by Stephen Lindow, an American researcher. He believes he has found a way to 'turn off' the bacterium's ice-creating abilities. It is an open question what effect the widespread adoption of such a technique to protect crops could have on local climates.

SULPHUR IN THE SEA

The sea has a distinct smell. We all know it, but what is it? Ozone? Salt? The answer is a chemical which, until a decade ago, few ocean scientists had heard of. It is dimethyl sulphide, or DMS. The gas is given off by algae, the ubiquitous single-celled plant life of the sea. They excrete about 60 million tonnes of it into the oceans each year. We do not know what DMS does directly for algae. But a posse of investigators believes that DMS may help prevent the Earth from overheating.

The discovery of the importance of DMS was made by Jim Lovelock, the inventor of Gaia. In 1971 he begged a place aboard a British research boat, the RV *Shackleton*, on its voyage from England to Antarctica and back. He took with him the most important of a number of pieces of equipment that he has invented, an electron capture detector. This is a supremely sensitive instrument for measuring tiny amounts of chemicals in the air. Never one to hide his successes, Lovelock later claimed that this device 'provided the background information about pesticides in the global environment which Rachel Carson used to write her book, *Silent Spring*, and so start the environmental revolution'.

On the RV *Shackleton*, Lovelock used the detector to measure for the first time CFCs in the ocean air. This, he says, led directly to the warnings three years later by Rowland and Molina about dangers to the ozone layer from CFCs. He also found, wherever the boat went, DMS. This observation took longer to come to fruition. But it culminated, in the summer of 1987, in a paper in *Nature* in which he, Meinrat Andreae and two American colleagues, Bob Charlson and Stephen Warren, first outlined their theory that DMS from algae may be acting as part of the global thermostat.

Most species of algae excrete DMS. The gas is converted in the air to tiny particles of sulphuric acid and ammonium sulphate which turn up in clouds over the oceans. More than that, those particles seem to be responsible for the formation of most of those clouds. Just as bacteria released by plants show ideal qualities as ice nuclei within clouds, so Andreae, Lovelock and their colleagues are now convinced that most of the condensation nuclei in clouds over the remote oceans are minute particles created from DMS bubbling out of the sea. They say that without the algae in the sea there would be no DMS, few sulphur particles, and far fewer clouds. Get rid of the clouds and the world would warm up. (That, as we saw earlier, may have been exactly what happened during the massive extinction 65 million years ago.)

Once Lovelock discovered DMS in the Atlantic Ocean air, it began to show up everywhere. Andreae sailed round the world measuring it. Andreae's former colleagues in Britain, Peter Liss and Susan Turner, tracked it down as the 'missing link' they had been seeking in the global sulphur budget.

Clouds, like ice and snow, are nature's reflectors. Sunlight bounces back off them right into space. Ocean water reflects only 10% of the Sun's radiation. But clouds reflect up to 60%. Lovelock and company argue that an increase of 30%

in the number of cloud condensation nuclei in clouds over the oceans would cut the Earth's average surface temperature by 1.3°C. 'I believe the mechanism is as large or larger than the carbon dioxide greenhouse effect,' says Lovelock. And, of course, it could operate in the opposite direction, cooling rather than warming.

The amount of light that a cloud reflects depends on the number of condensation nuclei it contains. A cloud with more nuclei is a more brilliant white. This is illustrated nicely by satellite photographs of the effect on clouds of smoke from ships' funnels. Far from blackening the clouds, the ships leave long, white, highly reflective trails in clouds. This is because the smoke doses the clouds with particles that make them whiter. DMS seems to do the same thing.

Even when they do not form clouds, the sulphur particles from DMS appear uncannily good at controlling temperature. The particles are less than a thousandth of a millimetre across, just the right size to interfere with and scatter sunlight, creating a kind of natural haze. Glen Shaw, an American researcher, told the conference on Gaia at San Diego:

> The particles are exactly the right size to remain in the atmosphere for long periods. And they are at a wavelength where the Sun's energy peaks, so that they have the maximum interaction ... How could you go about destroying our climate on a limited budget? I would use these particles to mess with the clouds.

Lovelock's *Nature* paper argued that algae are using DMS to regulate the climate to their own advantage. If it gets too hot, they produce more DMS to create more clouds, bringing temperatures back down. That is pure Gaia and the suggestion caused a furore. Even Lovelock's supporters say that there is no direct evidence that algae produce more DMS when it is hot. Lovelock and his co-authors point to the tropical oceans, where there are fewer algae floating around than in colder waters, yet where those algae produce more DMS than their counterparts in temperate waters. 'It appears that ... independent of the rate of primary production, the warmest, most saline, and most intensely illuminated regions of the oceans have the highest rate of DMS emissions to the atmosphere. This is a key fact.'

It is also fraught with confusion. There is probably more DMS in the tropical oceans because the types of algae that produce most DMS live there. This could be an accident, or Gaian design. At any rate, the biggest producers of DMS are in the best regions of the oceans to cut out sunlight and cool the planet.

A second issue goes to the heart of the argument about Gaia. Lovelock's paper puts the question baldly: 'How could the local activity of species living in the ocean evolve to serve the altruism of planetary regulation?' Beyond the question of how, is why. 'Why should an algal community of the ocean ... produce DMS for the benefit of, among other things, elephants and giraffes?'

The answer, the Gaians suggest, is that like other forms of evolution, it happened at first by chance. The complex chemical pathway which creates DMS in the ocean air starts with a chemical manufactured by algae called dimethyl sulphonate. This DMSP helps the algae in coastal waters to cope with excess salt. It is invaluable if, say, the algae dry out on beaches at low tide. Algae might have evolved to produce DMSP during ancient ice ages, when seas were lower and saltier. Once a colony of algae had evolved to produce DMSP, it would increase its own chances of survival. The colony would also be excreting a new by-product, DMS. You might call it pollution, but by chance it also formed clouds which protected the algae from the Sun. Natural selection could do the rest. The advantages would be especially great in the tropics.

The theory is plausible, but there is an obvious logical problem in arguing that chemicals now operating a thermostat were originally excreted to create more clouds during an ice age. That would make the world yet colder. But perhaps that is how it was. Ice cores from the Antarctic suggest that there was perhaps twice as much DMS around during the most recent ice age as today. Charlson thinks it could have deepened the ice-age freeze by about 1°C. That does not sound much like a thermostat in operation, but 'perhaps

Gaia prefers a colder climate,' says Lovelock, at his most enigmatic. 'Perhaps the sea biota may favour coolness, while land biota prefer warmth,' suggests Lovelock's British colleague, Andrew Watson. 'Perhaps in ice ages, the balance becomes weighted towards the interests of sea life.' The story of DMS remains full of perhapses.

Nobody has identified the exact processes that turn DMSP into DMS or DMS into its various sulphate derivatives. Some investigators, including Andreae, think methyl iodide, a chemical excreted by seaweed, may be necessary to make DMS. Bacteria may in turn convert the DMS to sulphate. Bugs, as ever, seem to be close to the heart of things. But the web could take a long time to unravel.

One important issue is whether humans might be encouraging the production of DMS. If we are, we might be counteracting the greenhouse warming. One place to look for evidence is the North Sea, which is surrounded by the industrial nations of Europe. Those nations bombard it with chemicals, especially fertilizers washing from fields. They could be feeding a growing population of algae in the sea. Peter Liss from the University of East Anglia spent part of 1988 on a research ship looking for algae and measuring DMS in the North Sea. He says that the sea 'has three times the average global production of DMS'. But the distribution is very patchy, depending on the flowering of patches of algae in spring and summer. Liss believes that the number of these algal 'blooms' in the North Sea is rising and that DMS from algal blooms, which are fed by fertilizers running into the North Sea, could be increasing cloud cover.

There is another aspect, says Liss. The sulphate particles are helping to turn the raindrops in the clouds to acid. He calculates that DMS from algae could be responsible for up to half of the acid rain falling over Scandinavia. Not surprisingly, Britain's Central Electricity Generating Board, Europe's largest producer of sulphate pollution, has set its researchers to verify his conclusions.

This line of inquiry is intriguing. If sulphate from DMS produces clouds, then so presumably does the sulphate from power stations. Worldwide, DMS is responsible for about half of the sulphur in the air. The other half, concentrated over the industrial nations of Europe and North America, comes from burning fossil fuels. Power stations have quadrupled the amount of sulphur in the air over the northern hemisphere. Is this sulphur making the hemisphere cloudier? Stephen Schneider, a climate modeller with a taste for new ideas, says this could conceivably explain why, in the decades from the 1940s to the 1970s, the northern hemisphere cooled down, while the southern hemisphere continued a century-long warming.

If sulphur does have a part in the global thermostat, then we could already be guiding it. It would be a fine irony to discover that one way of keeping the greenhouse effect at bay would be to redouble our efforts to create acid rain.

6

TURNING UP THE HEAT

IN THE HOTHOUSE

The inhabitants of planet Earth are quietly conducting a gigantic environmental experiment. So vast and so sweeping will be the consequences that, were it brought before any responsible council for approval, it would be firmly rejected. Yet it goes on with little interference from any jurisdiction or nation. The experiment in question is the release of carbon dioxide and other so-called greenhouse gases to the atmosphere.

The author of this invective, published in *Nature* in 1987, is Wally Broecker from the Lamont-Doherty Observatory at Columbia University in the US. His laboratory has pioneered the investigation of the role of oceans in the greenhouse effect. He warned that, despite the apparent sophistication of computer models, scientists know remarkably little about what the effect of a greenhouse warming will be on our planet. We are in no better position to make predictions, he said,

than are medical scientists when asked when and where cancer will strike a specific person ... We play Russian roulette with climate, hoping that the future will hold no unpleasant surprises. No one knows what lies in the active chamber of the gun, but I am less optimistic about its contents than many.

Turning Up the Heat

The man-made greenhouse effect is one of the great issues for the future of mankind. For many decades, the basic science behind it has been clear enough, but it has inhabited a kind of scientific limboland. Without some sign of its impact on the real world, the greenhouse effect seemed more religion than science.

Most of the gases in the atmosphere, including nitrogen and oxygen which make up more than 90% of the total, have little effect on the Earth's climate. Radiation passes through them without difficulty. But other gases, present in much smaller amounts, have a profound influence. These are the greenhouse gases. The two most important are water vapour, which makes up 4% of the volume of the atmosphere, and carbon dioxide. Other gases which, thanks to humans, have an increasing influence include methane, nitrous oxide and exclusively man-made chemicals such as CFCs, the scourge of the ozone layer.

The greenhouse gases trap heat from the Sun's radiation; they are a kind of one-way mirror. The gases are transparent to radiation at the visible wavelengths. This radiation, which includes most of the energy of sunlight, passes through the atmosphere and is absorbed by the surface of the Earth, which reradiates it as infra-red radiation. It is this radiation, emanating from the Earth's surface and otherwise destined to disappear into space, that the carbon dioxide traps in our global greenhouse. Each square metre of the Earth's surface emits an average of 390 watts. Satellites in space measure only 237 watts leaving the atmosphere. The result is a much warmer lower atmosphere than we would otherwise enjoy.

As we have seen, the greenhouse is no new phenomenon. It was at its most efficient in the early days of the Earth, when the Sun was weaker. Even today, however, without natural concentrations of carbon dioxide and water vapour in the atmosphere, the planet would be frozen, with an average temperature of minus 20°C, 35°C colder than today.

The first person to realize that gases in the atmosphere trap the Sun's heat was a Frenchman, Baron Jean Baptiste Joseph Fourier, who was born in 1768. He was a mathematician turned artillery officer who spent several years as

96

Napoleon's governor in Egypt. Later, he used his mathematical finding, Fourier's theorem, to develop new ideas about the flow of heat. During this work, he stumbled on the role of carbon dioxide in the atmosphere, which he dubbed the 'hothouse' effect. Unfortunately, in later life, his interest in heat became obsessive. He heated his home to absurd temperatures and swathed himself in layer upon layer of clothing, before one day he fell to his death down a staircase.

His ideas were pursued by a Swedish Nobel-prize-winning chemist, Svante Arrhenius. During the 1890s, Arrhenius calculated the effect on temperatures of doubling the amount of carbon dioxide in the atmosphere. He came up with a figure of 5°C and predicted that warming would be greatest at high latitudes. Modern investigators have barely altered that prediction. He also proposed that reduced amounts of carbon dioxide in the air caused ice ages — another idea ahead of its time.

Arrhenius had not suspected that humans might already have been working on a global experiment to test his calculation. The idea that mankind could alter the climate by burning fossil fuels and releasing trace gases in sufficient quantities was put forward by a British pollution scientist, G.S. Callendar, in 1938. But nobody took him too seriously. It was not until 1957 that Roger Revelle, a leading American oceanographer, revived the idea, coining the phrase 'large-scale geophysical experiment' to describe it. That year also, David Keeling, a young American researcher from the Scripps Institution of Oceanography in California, proposed setting up a continuous monitor of carbon dioxide in the air during the International Geophysical Year.

Thirty years on, that monitor, on top of Mauna Loa in Hawaii, remains one of the most important sources of data for investigating the greenhouse effect. The graph from the Mauna Loa monitor is a classic of atmospheric science. It shows an almost perfect wave pattern modulating each year with the seasons, but rising steadily at a rate of 4.5% per decade to reach average carbon dioxide levels a little above 350 ppm in 1988. From Keeling's data, Roger Revelle and modellers such as Syukuro Manabe and Richard Wetherald began to describe the likely consequences of greenhouse warming. And it led to other observers looking for and finding increases in other greenhouse gases in the atmosphere.

MAUNA LOA, HAWAII
Monthly average carbon dioxide concentration

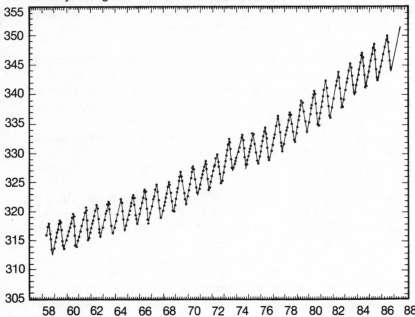

The inexorable rise of carbon dioxide. This is the 30-year plot of rising levels of carbon dioxide in the air at Mauna Loa in Hawaii. The seasonal wave is caused by plants releasing carbon dioxide in winter and taking it up in summer.

Many of these studies have been done from a network of fourteen research stations monitoring gases in the atmosphere. The stations are in remote spots well away from cities, from Alert on the north coast of Greenland and the South Pole, to Cape Grim in Tasmania and Laso Roca in Argentina, two stations that face each other across thousands of kilometres of the Southern Ocean.

Methane, which we will discuss in detail later, is accumulating in the air at a rate of 1% a year, more than twice as fast as carbon dioxide. CFCs, which molecule for molecule are 10,000 times more effective greenhouse gases than carbon dioxide, increased by 100% between 1975 and 1985. The accumulation of nitrous oxide, laughing gas, is much slower at around 0.2% per year. But the gas, like CFCs, lasts in the atmosphere for more than 100 years and production, for instance from tropical rainforests and bacteria that eat nitrogen fertilizers, is now a third more than destruction. So there are substantial further increases in concentrations of nitrous oxide in the pipeline about which we can do little.

The combined effect of carbon dioxide, methane, CFCs and nitrous oxide is expected by 2030 to be the equivalent of a doubling of carbon dioxide levels from pre-industrial concentrations. Work on the greenhouse gases and the likely consequences of their accumulation in the atmosphere has flowered in the past decade. But it took 50 years, almost to the day, from Callendar's prediction of greenhouse warming until a number of mainstream scientists, with academic reputations to defend, felt able to declare during a hot, dry summer in 1988 that 'the greenhouse effect has arrived.'

BLOWING HOT AND COLD

What will the greenhouse world be like? Much is expected of the sophisticated computer models, called general circulation models, which simulate in the language of mathematics how the climate works. The models are housed in large number-crunching computer laboratories, mostly in the US. Among the important laboratories are the National Center for Atmospheric Research in Boulder, Colorado; the Geophysical Fluid Dynamics Laboratory in Princeton, New Jersey; NASA's Goddard Institute for Space Studies in New York and Britain's Meteorological Office in Bracknell. They contain vast amounts of information about how the current climatic systems work, about the flow of heat from the equator in the atmosphere and oceans, about evaporation rates and vegetation cover, snow depths and greenhouse gases, as well as basic laws of physics, such as the conservation of energy, momentum and mass.

The question most asked of the models is: what will be the effect of increasing the amount of greenhouse gases in the air to twice the amount present at the start of the industrial revolution? This amounts to asking them to make a prediction of what the world will be like by the middle of the next century. According to most models, the effect will be to raise temperatures worldwide by around 4°C. Part of this is the straightforward effect of more greenhouse gases trapping more heat. Part is from reinforcing 'feedbacks'. The most important feedback in the models is the ice-albedo feedback, which accounts for about a third of the total global warming. It operates because ice, being white, reflects about seven times more of the Sun's energy than open water. A warmer atmosphere will melt ice and snow. Sea ice, including the Arctic ice cap, is only one to three metres thick and will melt first. But glaciers on land are also sensitive to small changes in temperatures and will retreat quickly.

The melting will expose land and sea that reflects less of the Sun's heat and absorbs more. This will reinforce the heating. Over the Arctic the very stable air will trap warmth close to the ice. The computers predict that temperatures could rise by 10°C or more around the edges of the Arctic ice pack and the great ice shelves of Antarctica. By the middle of the next century, huge amounts of ice could be melting, clearing the Arctic Ocean of ice each summer. That would have important political and climatic implications. The ocean would be open for oil extraction and shipping, including warships, while the loss of ice could upset climate systems further south.

More heat will evaporate more water from the oceans. The air in the global greenhouse will probably be wetter as well as warmer. The extra water vapour in a warmer atmosphere will have its own greenhouse effect. This second feedback will accentuate the warming. But here the models become confused. The extra water vapour will probably form extra clouds. Clouds are a great 'white hole' in the models. Nobody knows if extra clouds would increase or decrease the warming. Syukuro Manabe at Princeton predicts tentatively that in the global greenhouse there will be fewer clouds in the tropics, but more at middle latitudes.

Clouds do two things: they cool the planet by reflecting the Sun's heat back into space before it reaches the Earth; and they absorb heat radiated from the surface and reflect it back to the surface again, so warming the planet. Clouds are both a sunshade and a blanket. They cover roughly half the globe at any one time. If the greenhouse effect changed the extent of cloud cover, and if the sunshade or blanket became dominant, then the cloud feedback could swamp all the other effects of the greenhouse.

A critical factor could turn out to be the very high wispy cirrus clouds, often called mare's-tails, at the top of the troposphere, close to the stratosphere. Some people predict they will spread across the sky in a warmer world. Far from cooling the planet, they have a strong greenhouse effect. (One maverick investigator, Fred Singer from George Mason University in Virginia, believes that the formation of a blanket of cirrus cloud after a nuclear holocaust could turn nuclear winter into a 'nuclear heatwave'.)

A third influence in greenhouse warming comes from the oceans. By soaking up heat, the oceans will slow up the warming of the planet for several decades. That sounds comforting, but it also means that a degree or so of global warming is circulating in the oceans now, ready to surface at any time. Jim Hansen at NASA's Goddard Institute for Space Studies says that for this reason, whatever action we take now, the planet will be at least 0.5°C warmer by 2005 and 1°C warmer a few years later. The oceans also currently absorb about half of the extra carbon dioxide we are putting into the air. We have little idea what might control this capacity or how we might interfere with it for good or ill.

The roles of ice, clouds and ocean are all physical. They lend themselves to mathematical formulae. But a second series of feedbacks with far less predictable consequences may operate through the biology of the planet. As we have seen, marine life could involve itself in climatic change through the sulphur cycle by creating clouds. Climatic changes could perhaps destroy many of the world's forests and dump their stores of carbon into the atmosphere, thus reinforcing the warming. On the other hand, if the warming encouraged plant life it could prevent the expected rise in

101

carbon dioxide levels in the atmosphere from taking place. The models do not touch these problems, which we will return to later. For the moment, however, we have the models — 'murky crystal balls', as Stephen Schneider, one of the US's top modellers, calls them.

If we accept that the world will be around 4° warmer in 2030, we need to know how it will happen and who will bear the brunt of the changes. At the Climatic Research Unit at the University of East Anglia, they have looked in detail at what has happened so far in our greenhouse world.

The models say that the world should have warmed by up to a degree in the past century. During the 1980s it reached that target, but until at least 1975 there were only sporadic signs. The northern hemisphere cooled from the 1940s to the 1960s. The recent rise 'appears to be too large to be explained by the [greenhouse] effect alone,' says Phil Jones at the unit.

Jones wonders whether the geographical pattern of temperature change holds a clue to what is going on. His data for the northern hemisphere show that while temperatures rose over north-west Canada by 2° during the past twenty years (six times the average) and by 1.6° over western Siberia, they fell across much of Europe from Ireland to Greece and Scandinavia. European sun-seekers had little to complain about, since it became warmer over Spain and southern France; but in the twenty years to 1986, temperatures slumped by 0.6° in Scandinavia. Norway and Sweden are now almost a degree out of step with neighbouring countries. It also became cooler in eastern Canada and parts of Greenland. In the southern hemisphere parts of the Antarctic coast have cooled a full degree.

These findings are most unexpected. The ice-albedo feedback should, according to theory, accentuate that warming in regions near the poles, such as northern Scandinavia and Canada and the fringes of Antarctica. Yet overall, in the past two decades, there has been little warming in the polar regions of either the northern or southern hemispheres.

Jones notes that the areas of cooling are all close to the oceans, which normally have a strong influence on their climates. Perhaps the oceans have kept temperatures down.

If, as researchers suspect, the oceans are acting as a global heat sink, delaying warming for several decades, then perhaps this explains the continuing cooling in places with a maritime climate. But there is a snag. Why, in which case, has the southern hemisphere, which is almost entirely ocean, led the way in warming, with a steady rise in temperatures lasting for a century?

Hansen at NASA says that what is important is the increase in contrast between sea and land temperatures. This upsets wind patterns. 'The relatively slow warming of surface waters in the mid-Atlantic off the eastern US and in the Pacific off California tends to increase sea level [air] pressure in those ocean regions and this in turn tends to cause more southerly winds in the eastern US and more northerly winds in the western US,' he says.

Hansen's team predicts that by the 1990s, 'the man in the street' in many parts of the world will be able to identify warming. 'In the 1980s,' he says, 'the global warming is small compared to the natural variability . . . But by the year 2000 there will be an obvious tendency for it to be warm in more regions, and by 2029 it will be warm almost everywhere.' In a paper submitted for publication before the 1988 drought in the US, Hansen's team predicted from its models that 'during the late 1980s and in the 1990s there will be a tendency for greater than average warming in the south-east and central US and relatively cooler conditions or less than average warming in the western US and much of Europe.'

Changes in temperatures could be the least of our problems in the coming decades. Our warmer world will also be wetter. Manabe and Richard Wetherald from Princeton say that there could be 10% more rain by 2030. Tropical storms could be more intense and frequent. But their model predicts that most of the extra rain will fall in temperate latitudes. Perhaps this process is already under way. Jones and his colleagues at the Climatic Research Unit at the University of East Anglia reported in 1987: 'In Europe annual precipitation has steadily increased since the mid-nineteenth century, with well above average precipitation since the dry [and also cold] spell of the 1940s. Highest values overall were recorded in 1979.' In the Soviet Union, five of the ten wettest years of the past century had occurred since 1978.

Not all places will become wetter. Another prediction is that the dry desert belts of the tropics, from the Sahara and Kalahari in Africa to western Australia and New Mexico, will expand away from the equator, pushing other weather systems north and south as they go. Again, they may already be on the move. Northern Africa and the Middle East have certainly become more desiccated, especially in the summer growing season. The consequences for Ethiopia and other parts of northern Africa are all too well known.

The impact of changes in rainfall and evaporation on farmers and on civil engineering projects, such as flood prevention and dam building, could be far more important than changes in temperatures, especially in the early stages of the warming.

Surprisingly, the soils in many parts of the new 'warm and wet' world could become parched. There are two reasons for this. First, the extra heating over the tropics is expected to drive all weather systems polewards, including the low-pressure systems that race across the middle latitudes watering the world's grain belts. Secondly, the hotter weather and reduced cloud cover predicted for areas such as the American midwest will massively increase evaporation. Manabe says the snows will melt earlier in spring and that too will dry out soils. The US seems set for some of the worst economic effects, but there is a growing fear that 'dust bowl conditions' could soon afflict other key grain growing areas, including western Europe and the Soviet breadbaskets such as the Ukraine.

Peter Gleick from the University of California at Berkeley has looked at the predictions of several models for the Sacramento basin in northern California. The basin provides almost all the water for agriculture in the Central Valley of California which, he points out, is 'one of the most pro-ductive agricultural regions of the world'. The models all predict much less moisture in the soil in the summer growing season — 44% less, in one model. Gleick predicts 'major environmental and socioeconomic difficulties'.

The Colorado River, which over millions of years has

carved out the Grand Canyon in Arizona, provides some of the most intensively used water in the world. Along its path, waters are removed and returned again and again by farmers of alfalfa on the high plains of Colorado, by the cities of Los Angeles and Phoenix, and by the lettuce growers in the parched desert lands of the Imperial Valley near the Mexican border.

It is a common boast that the west was won not with the gun but with the Hoover dam and others along the Colorado. The states along the river have drawn up an elaborate treaty allocating rights to the twenty cubic kilometres of water that flows down the river in a typical year. They may like to know that in 50 years' time, according to Roger Revelle, one of the pioneers of the greenhouse debate, the average flow of the Colorado will be half what it is today.

Jaromir Nemec, who is in charge of water resources at the UN's Food and Agriculture Organization, says 'water shocks' could become widespread. In a river basin such as the Colorado 'a reduction in rainfall of 25% produces a decrease in runoff [to rivers] of about 80%, which means that, to maintain water supplies, four times as many reservoirs are needed.'

The spectre of the greenhouse should also be worrying the farmers of the southern republics of the Soviet Union. The waters from two rivers that drain into the inland Aral Sea, the Amu Darya and Syr Darya, irrigate some 70,000 square kilometres of cotton and fruit fields. The water is already over-used. The Aral Sea was until recently the fourth largest inland sea in the world, but it has lost 60% of its water in the past 30 years. An annual flow into the sea of 70 cubic kilometres is now reduced to fifteen cubic kilometres in a good year. In 1987 virtually no water reached the Aral Sea. The port of Muinak, once one of the most important fishing ports in the Soviet Union, is today 50 kilometres from the coast. In places, the coast has receded by 100 kilometres. Philip Micklin, from the Western Michigan University in the US, predicts that even if the rainfall stays at current levels, the lake will dwindle to 8% of its current size by early next century. The news that flows will probably decrease further in the coming decades may force the Soviet Union to revive plans to divert water south from its northward-flowing Siberian rivers to water the fields around the Aral and Caspian seas.

Other major rivers will run low, says Revelle. They include the Yangtze and Yellow River in China, the Tigris and Euphrates, on which the first civilizations of the Middle East were founded, the Zambezi, which waters Zambia and Zimbabwe and feeds the Kariba dam, and in Europe the Po, Rhône and Danube. Many believe that the declining flows of the Blue and White Niles, which in early 1988 seemed about to plunge Egypt's ambitious irrigation plans into crisis, may be an early effect of the greenhouse. The dramatic floods of that summer have not changed the long-term prediction.

There will be some winners in the water stakes. The Canadians are cock-a-hoop at the series of aces the greenhouse effect seems about to deal them. Barry Smit of the University of Guelph believes that as growing seasons extend and the North American rain belt moves north, 'the US corn and wheat belts could shift into Canada'. Ontario could become the world's new centre of grain production as dry soils cut output in most other countries. But other studies suggest the fields of Saskatchewan, currently Canada's most productive, could become parched.

With fields of corn invading the tundra, parts of Siberia could gain too, but at the expense of the Ukraine. The models predict that the great tropical rain-givers, the monsoons, will intensify. This will increase yields of rice, but Revelle predicts that 'large increases in the flows of the Mekong and the Brahmaputra rivers could lead to frequent destructive floods over wide areas of Thailand, Laos, Cambodia, Vietnam, India and Bangladesh.' The likely consequences of such a change were brutally exposed in September 1988 when high rivers flooded more than half of Bangladesh, including the capital, Dacca.

One region the models do not agree about is the Sahel, the drought belt of northern Africa. The place most in need of predictions about the future availability of water seems the least likely to get them. Some models predict that, from Mauritania to Ethiopia, north Africa will become drier. The current dry era, which is associated with a northward movement of weather systems that create rain, may be an early sign of the changes we can expect in the coming decades. Other models suggest that an intensification of the monsoons will bring more rain to the desiccated lands of Africa.

It would be nice to know. Such information might not help farmers and nomads surviving from season to season, but it would help governments to decide whether reservoirs which they plan to build along the River Niger, for instance, will ever fill, and whether they should help farmers to cultivate fields which may disappear into the sand.

The most hopeful sign for the Sahel comes from a look backwards to the last time the world was as hot as it is today. That was between 8,000 and 5,000 years ago. Almost all the world's tropical deserts from Asia to the Americas were much wetter then than today. It was a golden age for today's dry lands of Africa. Some researchers say that we could as usefully look backwards to such times for information about the future as into the hearts of computers. The past may not mimic all the variables which we would put into a computer model, but at least we know it happened.

Alayne Street of the University of Cambridge in England looked at the records of lake sediments from all over Africa, as well as Arabia and India. At the end of the ice age, 13,000 years ago, Africa was cold and desiccated. The great tropical forests had all but disappeared and were confined to a few refuges in West Africa and the upper reaches of the River Congo. The Sahara spread even further south than today. But within a few thousand years, he reports, lake levels were high everywhere, indicating that monsoons were penetrating deep into desert areas from Lake Chad in the Sahara to Rajasthan in India.

'Elephant, giraffe and antelope ranged unchecked over the Sahara.' Now it was the Sahara that was confined to a few refuges 'isolated by corridors of forest and swamp'. Fossils of hippopotamus and crocodile are widespread even in central Sahara. Remains of malarial mosquitoes and water snails, which carry diseases such as *schistosomiasis*, turn up from this era as far north as the Tibesti mountains, the baked heart of today's Sahara. This was when vast stores of 'fossil water' were laid down beneath the Sahara. They are now being discovered and tapped from huge underground aquifers. In 1984 Colonel Gaddafi announced a plan to spend $4 billion in the first phase of building a vast network of pipelines across Libya, to be called the 'Great Man-Made River'. It would transport this ancient water to towns, such as Sidra and Benghazi, along the Mediterranean coast. Gaddafi even talked of linking the entire system to the Nile.

Moid Ahmad, professor of hydrology at Ohio University and a veteran of Saharan oil exploration, identifies two ancient Libyan aquifers at Sarir and Kufra that are to be tapped. A third, at Fezzan, may follow. He says there are seven major water basins beneath the Sahara from the Atlas Mountains of Morocco to Egypt. (The big eastern aquifer is in the Negev desert, which is currently in Israeli hands.) The dream is that Libya, which was once the granary of the Roman Empire, could again become an exporter of wheat.

Meanwhile, scientists are discovering deep in the Sahara the remains of giant wadis which ran with water more than 5,000 years ago, but which today are buried by sand dunes. One wadi began in the Tibesti hills in southern Libya and flowed for 800 kilometres before giving out on the border between Libya and Egypt. Another, the Wadi Howar, once sprang from mountains in northern Chad and drained into the Nile, some 1,000 kilometres to the east. It was a vast river draining an area that today has an average of less than three centimetres of rain a year. Its sediments contain the bones of crocodiles, buffalo, elephants and other large mammals.

G'DAY GREENHOUSE

Graeme Pearman has a poster on his office door in Melbourne. It depicts what looks like a trio of white sharks basking in a blue sea. It is, Pearman explains, all that might be left of the Sydney Opera House within the next century, as the sea rises round it.

Australia was the first nation to take the greenhouse effect seriously. Pearman and Barrie Pittock, his colleague at the nation's Atmospheric Research Centre in Melbourne, have banged the drum to good effect in a country where people have cause to worry about the vagaries of climate. When I met them in May 1988, they were about to fly to Western Australia to address farmers near Perth who are worried about their future. Average rainfall in the south-western corner of Australia has declined by a fifth during this century, the 1980s had seen almost continuous drought, and now Pittock had suggested that dry weather could become an almost permanent feature there, inside the greenhouse. 'I have had calls from farmers saying insurance companies are refusing them cover for their crops after our warnings,' said Pittock. He was wondering whether to be less forthright in future.

Campaigning about the greenhouse has its difficulties. People become confused. Some believe that the predictions of a rise in sea level from the greenhouse effect has something to do with the ozone hole. 'They have got hold of the idea that the ozone hole lets in more heat, warming the planet and melting the Antarctic ice,' says Pittock. 'But I'd prefer that confusion to complete ignorance.' Unlike many scientists, Pearman and Pittock believe in the importance of public awareness, however imperfect. They are aware, of course, that a public concerned about the greenhouse effect is also a public likely to want its government to pay scientists to investigate it.

Pearman has masterminded the first comprehensive analysis for one country of the possible impacts of the greenhouse effect. His report, drawing together the wisdom of civil engineers, ecologists, farmers, economists and others, was published in late 1988. It took as its starting point the projections of the standard global circulation models for Australia, giving preference, Pearman admits, to those predictions which appear to coincide with existing climatic trends. 'We could be getting it all wrong,' he says, 'but the important thing is to attempt to assess the effects and to find out what aspects of Australian life are most vulnerable to climatic change.' Pearman assumes that by 2030 temperatures in Australia will be 2 to 3°C higher; that rainfall will be up 50% in summer, but down 20% in winter; that tropical cyclones will penetrate further south ('They could be reaching Brisbane by then,' he says); and that sea levels will rise by perhaps a metre. Winds, including those in cyclones, will become stronger.

Given this prognosis, the Western Australian Water Authority is worried. Rain-bearing depressions crossing the Indian Ocean will track further south, missing the state altogether. The rains will fail even more often than today and the flow in rivers in the south-west of the state will fall by a half. This would halve the water resources available to hard-pressed Perth and triple the cost of providing new supplies. The state's tentative plans to pipe water more than 1,000 kilometres from the north of the state may have to be brought forward. But that water could be too expensive to irrigate the parched fields south of Perth. Greater evaporation of water from soils and reservoirs could drastically reduce the water output of the Snowy River Scheme, a complex of reservoirs which supplies much of the water drunk in New South Wales and Victoria.

In New Zealand, on the other hand, they are rubbing their hands. Jim Salinger, from the country's Meteorological Service, predicts that warmer temperatures will open large new areas of upland for sheep grazing, and allow citrus and subtropical fruits to grow over large areas. There could be lots more kiwi fruit.

On Australia's beaches the tide will be coming in with a vengeance. Sands will be gobbled up as rising waters destroy nesting places for birds and turtles and make life less pleasant for wading birds. Cyclones will dash coastal defences and inundate sewers and drains. Meanwhile, mosquitoes will like the greenhouse Australia. They will bring tropical diseases from the swamps of Queensland to southern cities. In the short term, rising seas could encourage coral to grow and make the Great Barrier Reef even more attractive. But later, says the reef's Marine Park Authority, 'greater inundation and possible cyclonic activity will lead to serious erosion and even disappearance of reefs as increasing depth of water covers the reef tops.'

The ski slopes of Victoria and New South Wales will all but disappear as the snow line retreats by 100 metres of altitude for every degree of warming. A 2° warming would decrease snow cover by 270 square kilometres and destroy a thriving tourist industry. Meanwhile, electricity demand will fall in the warm winters, but rise when people turn up their air-conditioning in the sweltering summers.

The Alpine plants and animals of Tasmania and New South Wales, including many species of trees, will die out. The mountain pygmy possum lives in rocky screes in these mountains, sheltering beneath rocks on hot summer days. The possum will roast to death if, as predicted, temperatures stay above 30°C for more than a few days. Further north, the antilopine kangaroo currently ranges for more than 2,000 kilometres across northern Australia from Kimberley in the west to Cape ·York in the east. By 2030, areas with the climate that it currently inhabits will have dwindled to two small patches in Queensland. The rare long-footed potoroo would become extinct, say ecologists. And the drier air across much of the outback is likely to bring many more bush fires — perhaps doing more ecological damage than all the other effects put together.

None of these events will be catastrophic, provided they happen slowly, over decades. But the Earth is rarely like that. Change generally seems to happen in jumps, whether it is the end of ice ages or the seasonal shift in monsoon winds. The greenhouse is unlikely to be different. Even if it were, humans and nature both tend to respond not to gradual change but to catastrophes such as cyclones, drought or floods. Small changes in average temperature, rainfall or sea level can bring big changes in the frequency of such extreme events. The greenhouse effect may be making drought in the US much more likely, but it took the actual event in 1988 to force serious public discussion in the US about the greenhouse.

Pittock points out that a quite small shift in average rainfall (one standard deviation) can change the chance of a drought year from, say, one in twenty to one in four. The frequency of successions of extreme events, such as two years of drought, will increase even more rapidly. Successions of extreme events are, of course, far more damaging than single events — turning drought into famine, for instance. In

Finland in the 1690s a series of dry years, which were not on their own exceptional, killed a third of the country's population.

The same effect applies to runs of days of extreme weather. Many crops, such as corn in the US, are sensitive to a few successive days of extremely warm weather. A study by Stephen Schneider and others found that a 1.7°C increase in mean temperatures at Des Moines, Iowa, in the heart of the US grain belt, would increase threefold the likelihood of a run of five days with daily maximum temperatures above 35°C.

Even small warmings in the global greenhouse will cause events of currently outlandish improbability to happen at least once in a generation. If, for instance, the chance of drought for one year is today one in twenty, the chance of two consecutive years of drought is one in 400 years (a pretty remote possibility). If the chance of that one year drought shifts to one in four, then the risk of two years of drought plummets to one in sixteen years, or almost twice in a generation. A doubling of carbon dioxide levels in the atmosphere by 2030 is, according to one of Britain's top climatologists, Tom Wigley, likely to produce changes in temperature and rainfall of precisely this order.

7

STRANGE CASE
OF THE MISSING CARBON

CARBON RESERVOIRS

Carbon is the most important of half a dozen elements which are central to life and the Earth's life-support systems. It makes up half the solid matter in the human body. When the planet formed, all the carbon was in rock. It slowly reached the air, primarily as carbon dioxide, through volcanoes and other disturbances in the Earth's crust. Once on the surface, carbon swiftly became caught up in the business of life. Estimates of the proportion of the planet's carbon so far loosed from the depths into the thin green smear on Earth where life happens range from 1 to 5%. The air has only ever retained a tiny amount of the carbon released from these original rocks. Most of the carbon soon leaves the air again for the oceans or the land, where it helps form living organisms.

After several trips back into the atmosphere, it becomes incorporated into newly formed sedimentary rock. Sedimentary rocks comprise the accumulated geochemical detritus of the planet, laid down in layers in bogs on land or, more usually, on the bottom of oceans. Rocks formed in bogs contain carbon from putrefying vegetation. It is this carbon, turned into coal, oil and peat, that humans are now burning, so returning the carbon to the atmosphere. The rest of the carbon eventually reaches the oceans where, after taking part in the formation of marine organisms, it falls to the floor to form rock.

113

Michael McElroy at Harvard University describes the cycle this way: 'A carbon atom released to the atmosphere as a constituent of the odourless, invisible molecule carbon dioxide during combustion of fossil fuel will flit back and forth between plants, soil, air and water for approximately 100,000 years before eventually returning to the relatively quiescent reservoir of the sediments.' Ocean sediments, as we have seen, are not the end of life for carbon. Eventually, as the continents drift and ocean sediments are thrust under the continental plates, the carbon is released by volcanoes back into the air. Says McElroy: 'The average carbon atom has made the cycle from sediments, through the more mobile compartments of the Earth, back to sediments, some twenty times over the course of Earth history.'

The amounts of carbon in each of these natural reservoirs put the output of the world's power stations into perspective, and make all the more remarkable the effect of our puny interventions in the planet's carbon system. The burning of fossil fuels belches about five gigatonnes of carbon (a gigatonne is a billion tonnes) into the air each year. That is almost exactly one tonne per person on the planet. In all, the atmosphere contains about 700 gigatonnes of carbon; the planet's soils, forests and plant life hold a similar amount, with perhaps twice as much in soils as in plants. The sea waters hold some 40,000 gigatonnes, 60 times more than the atmosphere. So far, humans have located a mere 4,000 gigatonnes in coal and oil deposits. There may be more. But all these reservoirs pale beside the carbon in sedimentary rocks at the bottom of oceans. That total is around 70 million gigatonnes.

So far, humans have not learned how to interfere with plate tectonics or to stop volcanoes erupting. So we cannot alter the steady natural cycling of carbon into the air over the next few hundred years. But we can and are interfering with every other step in this cycle of carbon, either directly or through the greenhouse warming. And, with such large reservoirs of carbon involved, the potential for each of those steps in the cycle to respond in dramatic and unexpected ways is considerable.

Chopping down trees or polluting the oceans could upset

the carbon cycle in ways just as fundamental as pumping carbon dioxide into the air. The greenhouse warming could itself trigger events in the forests or oceans to neutralize the greenhouse effect, to accelerate it or even put it into an unstoppable reverse.

LOST IN THE FORESTS

The simple questions are often the hardest. Here is one: where does the five billion tonnes of carbon that we thrust through chimneys into the air each year end up? It begins by adding to the store of carbon dioxide in the atmosphere. But only around half stays there. The rest has gone missing. There are two ·possible bolt holes: vegetation on land, and the sea.

Since the mid-1970s a fierce row has raged between two camps of scientists about where the carbon dioxide has gone. In the blue corner, we have oceanographers and geo-chemists such as Wally Broecker from the Lamont-Doherty Geological Observatory at Columbia University in New York. They agree that the most obvious place for the bulk of the missing carbon to end up is beneath the waves. The sea, after all, holds far more carbon than the atmosphere or land. And nobody can yet measure directly the 'flux' of carbon dissolving into the sea from the air. But they argue that no more than two billion tonnes of carbon added to the air by burning fossil fuels permanently crosses the divide between air and the sea each year. The limit is set by the chemistry of the surface layers of the ocean and the speed of mixing of the ocean waters. The geochemists conclude that plants on land must be taking up carbon.

In the green corner, we have biologists such as George Woodwell of the Woods Hole Marine Biological Laboratory in Massachusetts. They cannot believe that the missing carbon is bolstering the planet's vegetation. Don't we all know, they say, that the sound of chainsaws is ringing through the great tropical rainforests of the Amazon, West Africa and Indonesia? Have we not seen the satellite photo-graphs of fires burning across the Brazilian rainforests? Forests and their soils contain about 90% of all the carbon on land. As the trees burn, the carbon is returning rapidly to the atmosphere. Wood that is turned into furniture, chopsticks or paper will yield up its carbon later, as it rots. When trees are burned, perhaps a quarter of the store of carbon in soils and on the floors of forests also returns to the air.

In the mid-1970s, the geochemists had the upper hand, but in 1980 the greens came storming back, due largely to the work of Woodwell and Norman Myers. Myers once worked for the UN Food and Agriculture Organization in its Forestry Department. But after retiring to set up an environmental consultancy in the Oxfordshire village of Headington in England, he compiled for the US's National Research Council a review of existing surveys of the destruction of tropical rainforests. He concluded that the global exertions of the modern woodchoppers, fire-raisers and chainsawmen were permanently destroying 40 hectares of forest each minute, or 220,000 square kilometres (almost the size of the United Kingdom) each year. This amounted to an annual loss of 2% of the plant matter on land. It implied that 4.2 billion tonnes of carbon was leaving the forests for the air each year. This was at a time when the oceanographers had estimated that land vegetation was absorbing around one billion tonnes of carbon a year.

Myers' report was a 'desk study'. He did not personally tramp through any rainforests counting trees. In many cases, nobody had. Most of his data was anecdotal or based on small study areas close to populated areas. But, with the National Research Council's name attached, the review carried weight and remained through the 1980s one of the most cited studies of deforestation. Biologists such as George Woodwell and Richard Houghton from Woods Hole backed Myers. These two men predicted in 1983 that the destruction of forests would unleash nine billion tonnes of carbon a year into the air, 'before forests are exhausted early in the next century'.

This was heady stuff, but it did not last. Serious questions soon arose about Myers' data. It turned out that he was assuming what he appeared to conclude: that there was no regrowth of forests in the areas cut down by modern shifting cultivators. The old harmony between cultivators and the forests had broken down, he said. This was an unsubstantiated assertion, but crucial to the study's message, since perhaps two-thirds of the area of rainforest chopped down, even today, is cleared by shifting cultivators.

Soon the National Research Council, apparently embarrassed at having taken sides in such a controversy, paid for a re-examination of Myers' figures. And so, in what amounted to a major climbdown, Myers, Woodwell, Houghton and others published a letter in *Nature* in the summer of 1985 in which they reduced by two-thirds their past calculation of the rate of permanent destruction of tropical forests. That brought down their estimate of the permanent loss of carbon to the air by this route to around 1.7 billion tonnes per year.

The study appeared to be an attempt to find a consensus among the factions. But Myers continued to argue that true shifting cultivation had all but vanished from the tropics. Most modern cultivators simply did not leave time for the forest to recover before they returned to slash and burn again, he said. But many other researchers disagree. They say that shifting cultivation still works in most places at most times. They have come up with estimates for the loss of carbon to the air of around one billion tonnes per year. This new figure, from a study by Charles Hall published in *Science* in 1988, still leaves unaccounted for some two billion tonnes of carbon a year, or 40% of all the carbon dioxide put into the air from chimneys. One place to look for this missing carbon is in forests outside the tropics. The woods of the temperate lands (Europe, the US, the Russian steppes and China) were remorselessly destroyed for a thousand years. But today, from the highlands of Scotland to the northern plains of China, foresters are replanting to meet the growing demand for paper and cellulose. The forested area of New England is 40% greater today than in 1890. The Soviet Union has two million square kilometres more land under forests than in 1960.

The trees in temperate forests today are drawing carbon from the air, as the tropics give up carbon. However, the soils beneath many temperate forests may still be releasing carbon. This is because the faster turnover of trees in these 'factory forests' keeps down the amount of carbon in the soil. The dense litter that sits on the floor of virgin forests is absent in modern plantations. Most trees in plantations are harvested many decades before they reach maturity. The serried rows of spruce trees in the Scottish highlands contain perhaps a third as much carbon per hectare as the ancient oak forests of England. Their fast growth means that they draw a lot of carbon from the air — but the short life of most of the wood once it is chopped down means that carbon soon returns to the atmosphere. While tree planting in the temperate lands must be taking up carbon, it is far from clear how much. Thus the mystery of the missing carbon remains.

'PLANTS MAY GET BIGGER'

How might Gaia respond to greenhouse warming? She would certainly attempt to bring temperatures down by taking carbon dioxide out of the air. Plants on land would be likely to take part in such a process. The extra carbon dioxide in the air may be 'fertilizing' the planet's vegetation, encouraging it to increase its rate of photosynthesis, that is, fixing more carbon from the air to grow more. This fertilization could be overwhelming the impact of the chopping down of forests. It could be where the missing carbon is going. Maybe.

Again, the blue and green camps disagree. Broecker believes that the fertilization effect is operating, moderating the greenhouse effect. When horticulturalists pump extra carbon dioxide into glass greenhouses, it usually makes plants grow bigger and faster. Woodwell calls this evidence for a fertilization effect from carbon dioxide 'naïve' and 'feeble'. Greenhouses are artificial environments where fertilizers and water are always on tap and temperature is controlled. In the world outside these factors limit the growth of most plants. For instance, in the tundra of Canada, Scandinavia and Siberia, where the great northern forests reign, there is often not enough nitrogen in soils to allow trees to grow faster. Woodwell insists that 'there is no evidence from natural populations that the 25 to 30% increase in carbon dioxide in the atmosphere over the past century has increased the general growth of trees.'

The evidence lines up on both sides of the debate. The *New York Times* had some purple prose for one nugget of research. 'Ancient gnarled pine trees struggling to survive in the mountains of Nevada and California have grown surprisingly fat, presaging momentous changes in the landscape of the Earth.' This portentous rhetoric was based on an observation by the Tree Ring Laboratory at the University of Arizona that the thin rings in the trunks of bristlecone pines have become thicker since around 1850. Each ring represents a year's growth, so the trees are growing faster. But who knows why?

In Australia researchers say they found from studies of tree rings that Tasmanian trees are taking up more carbon dioxide than earlier this century. More impressive is a study from the low-lying shires of England, published in 1987, which suggested that plants are responding to the presence of more carbon dioxide in unexpected ways. Ian Woodward from the University of Cambridge compares the number of pores on the leaves of trees collected today with those picked and put into a collection at the university's Department of Botany two centuries ago. Today, there are little more than half as many pores. Woodward suggsts that modern trees can gain all the carbon dioxide they need from the air through fewer pores. So they economize by growing fewer pores. This certainly suggests that plants are responding to changes in carbon dioxide levels, but by becoming more efficient, not bigger.

These isolated observations prove little. But the greenhouse men are unabashed. Herman Bouwer, as head of the US Water Conservation Laboratory in Phoenix, Arizona, had no hesitation in bringing the good news to a conference on water use in the twenty-first century: 'Greenhouse studies have shown that a doubling of atmospheric carbon dioxide content will increase crop yields by about one-third.'

The UN Environment Programme (UNEP), in a report on the greenhouse effect published in 1987, was equally gung-ho. It headlined one section: 'Plants will get bigger'. The report predicted that one of the two main categories of plants, called C3 plants after a key detail in their method of photosynthesis, could increase growth by between 10 and

50% by 2030. Cotton yields would increase by 100%. The second main category of plants, C4 plants, would benefit much less. This was largely good news. Most trees are C3 species, and sixteen of the world's twenty main food crops, including wheat, rice and barley, are C3 plants. Meanwhile, 'fourteen of the world's eighteen most noxious weeds are C4 plants,' said the UNEP. The bad news is that three of the four important C4 crops are maize, sorghum and millet, the staple foods of the poor arid countries around the Sahara. The fourth is sugar cane, a staple cash crop of many poor tropical countries.

The UNEP report reckoned 'it is quite possible that the spectacular recent growth in plant yields is partly due to increased levels of carbon dioxide in the air.' But before we get carried away by this vision of a future hothouse horticulture without the glaziers' bills, the UNEP report offers a caution. 'The food quality tends to deteriorate as carbon dioxide levels increase. Leaves become relatively richer in carbon and poorer in nitrogen.' So we would have to eat more to consume the same amount of protein, and pests would also eat more.

Many plants will see little benefit from carbon dioxide fertilization. Fruit trees, for instance, need winter frosts to germinate. No frost: no trees. And more carbon dioxide will not help the grain belt of North America, the world's breadbasket. Extra carbon dioxide will make the cereals mature more quickly, which will reduce yields. The kind of increases in crop yields that are possible under glass may prove an illusion in the fields.

In this climate of uncertainty, some aspects of the UNEP's report verge on the farcical. In Iceland, one end result of carbon dioxide fertilization, it suggests, 'would be an increase in the carcass weight of lambs, estimated at some 11%'. Don't hold your breath.

The big issue for the future of the planet has less to do with the growth rate of food crops and more to do with forests, where most of the terrestrial carbon resides. How will the world's forests respond to the warmer, carbon dioxide-rich world? Will they damp down the greenhouse effect by absorbing carbon, or accelerate it by releasing carbon?

Woodwell, ever the pessimist, argues that any increase in the uptake of carbon dioxide by photosynthesis during the day will be swamped by releases of carbon dioxide by respiration at night. This is a process by which plants break down their body matter, such as carbohydrates, to create energy. At the same time, they release carbon dioxide. Respiration increases when plants are under stress. If the greenhouse increases respiration more than it does photosynthesis, a potentially highly-damaging positive feedback could have begun.

During the 1960s, Woodwell worked on a study at the US's Brookhaven National Laboratory which found that on warm nights the amounts of carbon dioxide in forest air rose, because the trees respired more. If that happened on a planetary scale the global greenhouse would take on a rather different perspective from that proposed by the UNEP.

'A 10°C increase in temperature . . . commonly induces a change in the rate of respiration of 1.5 times to more than 4 times,' Woodwell says. He warns that the warming expected for the next 20 to 30 years in Europe and North America 'could easily double the rates of respiration in the current biota, including soils . . . When respiration outstrips photosynthesis, plants and other organisms cease growth and ultimately die.'

Both sides in this argument seize on evidence that the seasonal variation in carbon dioxide levels in the atmosphere increased by 15% between 1975 and the late 1980s. The seasonal wave in the carbon dioxide graph is caused by the uptake and release of carbon by plants, especially trees. Forests away from the tropics release carbon into the air in winter and take it back in summer. Richard Gammon, from the US government's Pacific Marine Environmental Laboratory in Seattle, says that the increasing magnitude of the annual wave shows that 'the system is breathing harder. We are seeing a seasonal imbalance of photosynthetic uptake of carbon.' He believes this means that 'the biosphere is sick.' But it could also mean that the biosphere is increasingly healthy, revelling perhaps in the extra carbon dioxide and the warmer climate.

Rosanne D'Arrigo from Columbia University in New

York has investigated how the great forests of northern Europe, Siberia and Canada, known as the boreal forests, 'breathe' carbon dioxide in and out each year. These ancient forests cover a strip of land around 1,000 kilometres wide across three continents. There are six million square kilometres of boreal forests, and they make up 14% of the world's forest biomass. The remote lands where boreal forests reign — around Hudson Bay, through the Yukon and in the frozen wastes of Siberia — have seen some of the biggest increases in average temperatures in the past century, and they are where computer models predict the greatest effects of greenhouse warming in future. If they start to suffer, then the carbon cycle could be in real trouble.

In the northern forests, growth shuts down in winter and spurts again when the summer suns come. D'Arrigo reckons that 'the seasonal growth of the combined boreal forests of North America and Eurasia accounts for about 50% of the mean seasonal carbon dioxide amplitude at Point Barrow, Alaska, and about 30% of the more globally representative carbon dioxide signal at Mauna Loa.' She also claims that in the years when tree rings reveal strong growth in the forests of northern Canada, there is also a larger than normal seasonal change of carbon dioxide concentrations measured at Point Barrow. This has led optimists to predict that the global increase in the seasonal variation is a sign of a healthy future for the northern forests. The trees are breathing hard because they are healthy. The optimists look forward to a northward march of trees, taking the forests up to 1,000 kilometres further into the Arctic. And they expect up to 50% more growth inside the forests. This would take carbon dioxide out of the atmosphere and damp down the greenhouse effect. Barrie Pittock, Australia's leading investigator of the greenhouse effect, says that just a 1% increase in the carbon in live vegetation worldwide would offset the current releases of carbon dioxide from burning fossil fuels.

The pessimists see the same evidence and argue the precise opposite. Some climate models predict that even as the northern limit of the forests extends towards the poles, the warmer temperate lands will extend north to squeeze the forests into a much narrower strip of land than they occupy today. One study concluded that the climatic zone occupied by northern forests would diminish from 23% to 1% of the land surface of the planet.

A key problem is the speed of change. Trees die more quickly than they can colonize new land. Jim Hansen at NASA says the speed of warming predicted by his models implies a poleward shift of climate zones of 50 to 75 kilometres per decade. 'This is faster than most plants and trees are thought to be capable of naturally migrating.' It is easy to imagine that a slow spreading of trees into the tundra could be overwhelmed by a short-term destruction of the forests at their southern edges.

WALDSTERBEN AND THE GREENHOUSE

Since 1983, the forests of Europe and North America have been hit by a strange and widespread sickness. Foliage has turned yellow and thinned drastically, roots have shrivelled and, in exposed areas on hilltops, entire forests have died. Some of the worst destruction has been in West Germany, where the damage is called '*Waldsterben*'. There a forest ecologist, Bernhard Ulrich, first warned in 1982 that the trees were sick. 'After the next warm, dry years, the forest damage will drastically increase,' he said. And he was right. Two warm, dry years followed and, by 1985, more than half West Germany's trees were showing signs of decline, and a fifth of them were seriously affected. Since then, the sickness has persisted in Germany and spread across the Alps to France, Switzerland and Austria, north into the Netherlands and Sweden and possibly to Britain. Similar symptoms have appeared widely in North America. Ulrich blamed acid rain and especially the way it acidified soils, a phenomenon now recognized all over Europe. Others have pointed to the growing concentration of other air pollutants. But all investigators agree that the rapid decline of the mid-1980s was triggered by the warm dry years of 1983 and 1984. The year of 1983 was exceptionally hot and dry in the middle latitudes of the northern hemisphere. Kenneth Hare, the chairman of Canada's Climate Program Planning Board, says such a year 'resembles what will be normal five decades from now'. If he is right, then global warming will push the trees of Europe and North America towards greater respiration. It is an alarming thought. John Harte from the Energy and Resources Group at the University of California at Berkeley says: 'In my view, the phenomenon of *Waldsterben* is the biggest ecological transformation now in progress on the planet.'

David Keeling, the man who set up the carbon dioxide monitor at Mauna Loa in 1958, describes a blip on his graph in 1983. As bush fires raged in Australia and the trees of Europe and North America sickened, 'we saw four billion tonnes of carbon released by the land biosphere.' Satellites monitored that release and found that some at least came from forests in the US afflicted by *Waldsterben*.

Woodwell is not sure of the role of the greenhouse in *Waldsterben*. But, he says:

> This sudden destruction of forests ... is but a sample of the destruction that appears to be in store as the climate changes ... [It] will almost certainly result in a substantial further release of carbon into the atmosphere. The amount of release is difficult to estimate, but it has the potential of releasing hundreds of billions of tonnes of carbon over years to decades ... Such releases will accelerate the warming.

The contrasting images of the prospects for the planet's forests from global warming could not be more stark. The optimists say that warming and carbon dioxide fertilization will see the trees prospering. The great northern forests could spread further into the Arctic and grow at an unheard-of pace. This would consume carbon and stabilize the greenhouse warming. Woodwell and the pessimists conjure up a picture of forests from the Arctic to the Amazon being destroyed by changing climate at a rate that man could not conceive of achieving with chainsaw or fire. We have, in truth, no idea which is right.

8

THE SHAPE OF THINGS TO COME?

ACTS OF GOD

Melbourne is noted more for its drizzle than its dust storms. Australia's second largest city lies beneath the track of rain-bearing depressions that blow across southern Australia from the Indian Ocean. But one afternoon in February 1983, the sky turned black over the city as dust storms raged. It was the height of the worst drought in Australia for a century, and the height of the worst upset to the climate of the Pacific region for perhaps hundreds of years. In Melbourne, despite the black skies, the temperature, at 43°C, was the hottest ever recorded there.

A week later, bushfires rushed across the east side of Australia, killing more than 90 people. The year-long drought, which cost a quarter of the country's wheat crop and spread corpses of dead cattle and sheep across the parched land, cost farmers almost A$2 billion.

There were droughts, too, in southern Africa, India, Sri Lanka and as far east as Hawaii. More than 200 people starved to death in New Guinea. Bush fires spread through Java and Sumatra sending elephants rampaging through villages in search of water. Fires destroyed most of the forests of East Kalimantan and North Borneo. Yet on the eastern shores of the Pacific, in the South American countries of Ecuador and Peru, the same months brought devastating rainfall. About 260 centimetres of rain fell in six months at Guayaquil on the coast of Ecuador, almost twice the previous record. It was the worst disaster in the city since an earthquake flattened it in 1942. Much of the Ecuadorian coast flooded. Rain poured on to the Sechura desert of north-west Peru, where rainfall was up to 340 times the average. Off the coast, in the Galapagos Islands, more rain fell in two weeks in January 1983 than in the whole of the previous six years.

To the north, storms spread down the western coast of Canada and the US, lashing the coast of California, washing caravan parks into the sea and disrupting a royal visit by Queen Elizabeth of England. Blizzards hit the normally arid mountains of Arizona and New Mexico.

In the middle of the Pacific Ocean, the tranquil paradise of French Polynesia was hit by cyclones six times in as many months. They were the first cyclones to hit the islands for 75 years. In Tahiti, rainfall was eight times the average. On the other side of the world, in Africa, these turbulent months saw the start of the killer droughts that struck Ethiopia and the Sahel region. The winter of 1982–83 was also exceptionally warm in North America and much of Europe and the *Waldsterben* tree epidemic began.

All these events, we now know, were intimately connected. They formed part of a temporary shift in the ocean and wind in the Pacific, which ultimately influenced much of the planet. Similar shifts occur every three to five years, but the shift in 1982–83 was probably the most severe for a century. These massive perturbations to the weather systems of the Pacific are known to climatologists as ENSO events. ENSO is an acronym standing for *El Niño* (the oceanic part) Southern Oscillation (the atmospheric part). ENSO events are, say climatologists, the most serious disruptions to the global patterns of wind and sea this side of the ice ages.

Anybody who has made waves in a bathtub can understand the essence of ENSO. 1982–83 was the occasion when the water slopped out on to the bathroom floor. Under normal circumstances, the trade winds of the tropics blow from east to west across the Pacific (i.e., from South America to Indonesia). The winds drive the ocean, building up water on the western side of the ocean so that the sea level is typically about 40 centimetres higher in the west than in the east.

In the months before an ENSO event, the winds usually intensify, building up more warm water in the west. Then, suddenly, the winds slacken, or even reverse, and a great wave of water slops back eastwards. The wave, known as a 'Kelvin wave', travels at between 200 and 400 kilometres a day. It can be up to 2,000 kilometres wide, straddling the equator.

ENSO events may have been happening every few years for millenniums. Anthropologists believe that, hundreds of years ago, Pacific islanders rode these Kelvin waves to colonize the islands of Polynesia. Studies of an ENSO event in 1976 found that the wave took warm water east at a maximum rate of 30 million cubic metres a second.

In normal times, the coastal waters of Peru and Ecuador are a centre for the upwelling of cold water from the ocean depths. This water, known as the 'Humboldt current', drives north 'from the southern tip of Chile, bringing nutrients which support massive amounts of fish life, including what was once among the world's most important fisheries, the Peruvian anchovies. The massive influx of warm water from the west stops this upwelling, destroys the fishery and has a serious impact on the wildlife and local economies of the eastern Pacific.

El Niño means 'little boy', a name coined because the currents usually appear off the South American coast around Christmas. The *El Niño* of 1982, however, showed up in the last week of September. Sea temperatures rose by 4°C within 24 hours.

By cutting out the Humboldt current, *El Ninō* reduced the amount of life in the ocean to between a fifth and a twentieth of normal. That was bad news for the bird colonies which are as dependent on local fish as the Peruvian fishing fleets. The blue-faced booby was the first aerial victim. In June 1982, before the Kelvin wave arrived, ornithologists recorded the booby meeting as normal on Christmas Island. As the warm water swept round the island in September, it destroyed the birds' food supplies. When the ornithologists returned in November, only three adult birds and one underweight nestling remained. In June, there had been 20,000 great frigate birds on the island. By November there were fewer than 100. Squid, their prime food, had deserted the island's waters. Frigate birds abandoned their nests throughout the tropical central and eastern Pacific.

On the arid Galapagos Islands, where warm seas triggered record rains for eight successive months, confused finches bred continuously throughout the rains. Scientists studying the after-effects of *El Niño* on the island where Darwin developed his theories of evolution, found that it had upset the processes of natural selection among a species known as Darwin's finches. The rains had spawned large numbers of small seeds. Small birds were in their element for several years. There were other beneficiaries. Giant tortoises and iguanas, along with all manner of insects, luxuriated in the green vegetation. But all the fur seal pups born in 1982 had died by March 1983. Their mothers stayed at sea for an average of five days, rather than the usual one or two, searching for food. But 'when they returned to shore they were unable to provide enough milk to prevent puppies from starving,' said a report in *Science*.

Humans also suffered from the disappearance of the fish. More than a billion dollars' worth of fish were simply not there when the trawlers arrived at the fishing grounds. Hake went first. They live on the sea bottom and, when the cold waters disappeared, the fish moved with the water away from the coast. Large numbers of corbina floated dead off northern Peru. Their home waters were 8°C hotter than normal. In January 1983 sardines disappeared from the Ecuadorian coast and reappeared off Chile, where they could find plankton to eat.

Peruvian anchovies were once the basis of the world's largest fishery. The fish feed on the plankton in the up-welling cold waters and are typically the worst affected victims of *El Niño*. In the early 1980s the fish were already under threat from overfishing. The 1982–83 *El Niño* devastated the remaining fish and the fishery has never recovered.

While the cool and dry eastern Pacific becomes hot and humid, so the rains fail in the usually wet west. In normal times the winds from the east track across the Pacific to

Indonesia and Australia where they meet the warm ocean. That triggers some of the most intense tropical storms in the world — the kind that can make air travel over Indonesia distinctly bumpy. The updraughts of hot wet air and the release of heat as sea water evaporates in the region around Indonesia provide one of the three centres where the heat of the tropics is circulated to the rest of the atmosphere. There are similar areas of updraught over the basins of the rivers Congo and Amazon. But the one over Indonesia is the only one which can move. And it does.

During ENSO events, the air circulation system moves in harness with the ocean's circulation, though it is not clear which leads the way. As the east winds cut out, so does the updraught of air over the western Pacific. Instead, the winds begin to blow from west to east and the zone of updraught moves to the eastern Pacific.

This is where the Southern Oscillation, the other half of ENSO, comes in. In normal times, rising air in the western Pacific leaves behind low air pressure at the surface, while descending air (the norm in the eastern Pacific) creates high pressure. One of the earliest discoveries about the atmospheric circulation over the Pacific was that the 'normal' regime of low pressure in the west and high in the east occasionally reverses. For many decades, nobody realized that this phenomenon, known as the 'Southern Oscillation', was connected to *El Niño*, which was thought to be a local ocean phenomenon restricted to the eastern Pacific.

The pressure oscillation is traditionally described by the Southern Oscillation Index, a measure of the difference between air pressure in Darwin, northern Australia, and Tahiti in the eastern Pacific. ENSO events bring high pressure over Darwin. The high pressure prevents the growth of tropical storms and often extends far enough south to prevent the passage of rain systems from the Indian Ocean across southern Australia. These are the two main sources of rain in Australia. So Australia is vulnerable to drought during ENSO events.

Indeed, the Southern Oscillation is the main reason why the Australian climate is unusually variable. Neville Nicholls from the Australian Bureau of Meteorology says that ENSO events are often followed by anti-ENSOs as the oceans 'overshoot' on their way back to normal. Anti-ENSOs bring wet years to India, Australia and parts of Africa and eastern Asia, and a colder than usual eastern Pacific. During 1988 there was a particularly intense anti-ENSO which brought record rains over eastern Australia in early 1988 and extensive flooding in parts of southern China followed by the devastating floods in Sudan as rains deluged the Ethiopian highlands where the Blue Nile rises, and in Bangladesh.

Once an ENSO event is under way, it has a life of its own. But finding the cause is a major task. A phenomenon capable of linking ocean currents in the eastern Pacific with droughts in southern Australia, heatwaves in Europe and the flows of water in the River Nile is clearly a tough nut to crack.

Most researchers bet that the answer lies in the oceans. The sea has such great potential to hold and release heat that it seems likely to be dictating to the winds, rather than vice versa. British researchers at the Meteorological Office in Bracknell strengthened this feeling by developing a technique based entirely on sea surface temperatures which can predict, several months ahead, drought in Ethiopia and Sudan.

Several groups of scientists have constructed models of ENSO events. Stephen Zebiak and Mark Cane, from the Lamont-Doherty Geological Observatory of Columbia University in New York, successfully predicted the 1986–87 ENSO event nine months in advance (at the conception, as it were, of the 'little boy'). They did it by monitoring wind direction and plugging the figures into their model. They say that 'ENSO's consequences are global: but the interactions vital to its existence all occur in the tropical Pacific region.'

The current theory about the genesis of ENSO events is that they are a natural consequence of the wind blowing water into the western side of the Pacific. They form part of a continuous cycle in which one ENSO event leads inevitably to the next. The sequence goes like this: the Kelvin wave travels east along the equator at up to 400 kilometres per day, crossing the Pacific Ocean in about two months. It is balanced by a second wave known as a 'Rossby wave', flowing slightly away from the equator, which tracks

The Shape of Things to Come?

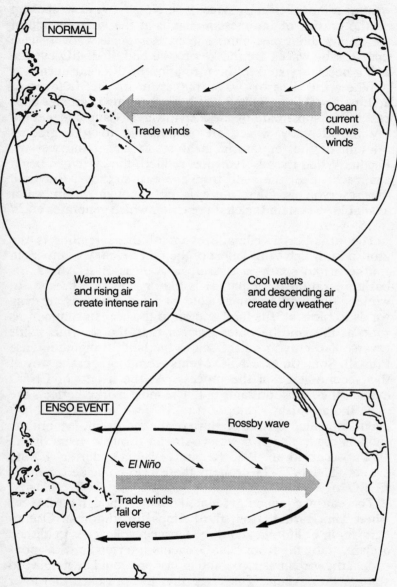

How the winds and waters of the tropical Pacific Ocean are transformed by ENSO events.

west at a more leisurely pace. The Rossby wave washes up on the barrier of Indonesian islands at the western side of the Pacific about nine months later. Researchers now believe that Rossby waves are the key to the end of ENSO events, and a necessary step in the formation of the next event.

When the Rossby wave makes it to the Indonesian archipelago it literally bounces back, heading at greater pace east in the slipstream of the Kelvin wave. Cane and Zebiak say that Rossby waves are responsible for the gradual refilling of the 'equatorial heat reservoir' in the western Pacific. When the reservoir has refilled, the cycle can begin again whenever the wind from the east slackens. But until the reservoir is filled there is not enough warm water available to sustain the chain reaction which generates an *El Niño* event.

The other great climatic event of these regions is the monsoon, which brings most of the rain to many countries in southern and south-east Asia, as well as East Africa. Its basic operation is simple. It is like a giant sea breeze. In winter, the land becomes cold and air descends, forcing winds to blow off the land and on to the sea. In summer, as soon as the land becomes warmer than the sea, the winds reverse and blow from the sea to the land, bringing intense rainfall. Sometimes, ENSO events seem to get in the way of this second stage of the process. At the height of ENSO events, the monsoon rains fail. The most marked effects are over India and in Ethiopia. In 1877, when a large ENSO event coincided with the failure of the monsoon, five million Indians died. The two worst African drought years of the 1980s occurred in 1982–83 and 1986–87, during ENSO events. The 1972–73 drought there also coincided with an ENSO.

This causal connection seemed obvious enough until 1987, when Tim Barnett from the Scripps Institution of Oceanography in California and three German colleagues published a claim that, far from ENSO events interfering with monsoons, the mechanisms behind monsoons could be helping to start ENSO events. They said that the presence of winter snow over the giant land mass of Asia and Europe, and especially the Himalayas, was 'intimately connected' to

ENSO. The results, they said, 'challenge the current dogma ... suggesting the processes over continental land masses may also have to be considered,' along with events at sea.

The role of snow in the Himalayas in the monsoon system was first suggested more than a century ago by a British climatologist called Henry Blanford. As Barnett summarized it: 'The presence of the snow, its melting, and evaporation of its meltwater retard and diminish warming of the Asian land mass and subsequent establishment of the land-sea temperature contrast that drives the monsoon circulation.' Delay the warming with a heavy winter snow and you have a delayed or weakened monsoon.

How could this influence ENSO events? One possibility is that if the monsoon does not get going, it cannot dissipate the heat building up in the tropical ocean around Indonesia. Instead, as the tropical easterlies find their way blocked, they falter and the ocean's heat heads back east. An ENSO event has begun.

In 1985, a ten-year international scientific effort began to trace the cause of ENSO events. It is called 'TOGA' (for tropical ocean-global atmosphere) and takes as its starting point the assumption that ENSO events are triggered by ocean-atmosphere interactions in the tropical Pacific. If Barnett and his colleagues are right, that project may be heading up a blind alley.

ENSO events reveal much about the complexity of the world's climate systems and how closely they are linked. One of the more important effects of greenhouse warming may be to change these systems, most likely in ways that will be extremely hard to predict. For Barrie Hunt, Australia's leading climate modeller, ENSO events are a crucial part of his country's weather. 'Droughts in Australia are almost always associated with ENSO events,' he says.

They dominate our weather. My fear is that the greenhouse effect could drag the Pacific towards an almost permanent ENSO. That would be disastrous for Australia.

It would also have serious repercussions round the world, bringing the kind of dry and warm conditions which Europe experienced in 1983, the year that *Waldsterben* began in earnest.

Nobody has any idea what the consequences of the greenhouse effect would be on ENSO events. It could reduce the temperature difference between the waters of the east and west Pacific and so damp down ENSOs. Or it could warm the western Pacific further, as Hunt suspects, and bring on more frequent and more intense ENSO events. We know that the warm years of 1983 and 1987 were both ENSO years. That may mean only that ENSO events add a little to a year's temperatures. But could they have a more lasting effect? Richard Gammon in the US believes that ENSOs may help 'ratchet' the climate to a warmer state. In 1983, as we have seen, forest fires and the dieback of trees in Europe and the US caused a flood of carbon into the atmosphere, which would have exacerbated the greenhouse, at any rate for that year. Also, the World Meteorological Organization reported that warm ocean temperatures round the world during ENSO events warm the atmosphere as well. During the anti-ENSO event of 1988, scientists were busy investigating whether it would have the opposite effect, winding world temperatures back down again. If both Gammon and Hunt are right, then we have a positive feedback in operation of the kind that Woodwell worried about for the northern forests.

The modellers are silent on this. The big climatic models do not take account of ENSO events. But, ominously, Jim Hansen's model at NASA predicts that among the places with the fastest warming in the next decade or so is likely to be the equatorial Pacific, the heart of the ENSO phenomenon.

9

THE CAUSES OF ICE AGES

SECRETS OF VOSTOK

The fascination of the Antarctic for scientists is unending. Locked away by winter ice in the last great untouched wilderness on Earth, the scientists from the national surveys of Britain, the US, Argentina, the Soviet Union and the rest often take on an unworldly demeanour. The science journal *Nature* spotted it. 'Those who have spent time in Antarctica seem to be something of a breed apart,' wrote journal staffer Philip Campbell, 'not least because they generally return to "civilization" itching to depart southward again at the earliest possible opportunity. This phenomenon must stem from some personal experience denied to less hardy mortals — the memory of a brilliant landscape of white and blue beneath an incomparably clear atmosphere, perhaps, or the attainment of as perfect a silence as nature will allow.'

The scientists are there partly as an act of political expediency. For the people of Washington and the Politburo, the scientists are staking a claim to the mineral wealth beneath the ice. Whitehall has another purpose. In the mid-1980s, the British government under Margaret Thatcher lopped large sums from its overall research budget. Yet the British Antarctic Survey, almost alone, prospered as Thatcher bolstered Britain's presence in the South Atlantic after the war with Argentina.

Whatever the motivations, under this political patronage good scientific work has been done. The British discovered the ozone hole after almost 30 years of diligent monitoring

135

from the British research station at Halley Bay. Less remarked, but perhaps of equal scientific importance, has been the work of the Russians at Vostok. There, between 1980 and 1985, they painstakingly drilled a tube, ten centimetres across, for more than two kilometres into the ice pack. The ice core they extracted captured a continuous record of the chemistry of the snow which has fallen there for the past 160,000 years, right through the most recent ice age and into the previous one.

The Soviet scientists handed their ice cores to French analysts led by Claude Lorius. In 1987 Lorius published the first results of an analysis of elements in the ice that could ultimately explain the origins of the ice ages. The analysis provided a year-by-year record of the temperature and chemical composition of the air at Vostok, which revealed that changes in temperatures and levels of carbon dioxide were sudden and dramatic, especially at the end of the ice ages. Most intriguingly, it also revealed an almost exact correlation between temperatures and carbon dioxide.

Carbon dioxide levels rose by around 50% within a few hundred years at the end of both ice ages. At the same time, temperatures soared. Coming on top of Swiss analysis of data from a shorter ice core taken from Greenland, the data provided strong evidence for a fundamental link between the global climate system and the carbon cycle. The results do not show whether changes in temperature cause changes in carbon dioxide or vice versa. One idea is that a small change in temperature triggers a bigger change in carbon dioxide, which then drags temperatures along after it.

Whatever the precise mechanism, it seems to be on a hairspring. Just 13,000 years ago, the planet was still in the grip of the last ice age. Vast ice sheets stretched down from the Arctic to cover Canada, much of the northern US and Britain as far as Oxfordshire. Four thousand years later, the planet was basking in a climate warmer than today. There is now evidence that, within that period, changes in temperature happened in surges, lasting perhaps only a few decades.

There have been about ten ice ages in the past million years, coming roughly every 100,000 years. Each seems to have crept up on the planet gradually, as ice packs accumulated, but to have ended with a bang. If we can understand this process, it may provide clues to how the planet will respond to a greenhouse warming. Thanks to mankind's influence, concentrations of carbon dioxide in the air today are about to rise above the maximum of any recent warm period between ice ages, the 'interglacials'. This will be a severe jolt to the system, since the 'natural' cycle passed its warmest point about 5,000 years ago and should now be progressing towards another ice age. As we head into territory uncharted by the planet for perhaps millions of years — an era now being dubbed the 'super-interglacial' — we need to know how the planet will respond. In particular we need to know whether the planet will amplify or damp down our initial warming.

PLANETARY WOBBLES

A fundamental feature of the long-term trends in climate is a cycle of wobbles in the orbit of the Earth. The phenomenon was first suggested in the 1870s by James Croll, an amateur Scottish scientist from humble origins. It was refined and developed in the 1920s by the man whose name it now bears, a Serbian mathematician called Milutin Milankovitch. There are in fact three separate wobbles, each with their own frequency. First, the tilt of the Earth's axis relative to the Sun varies between about 22° and 25° in a cycle which repeats itself every 41,000 years. A change in tilt changes the amount of the Sun's heat that strikes the polar regions. A second wobble is called the 'precession'. This determines the season at which the Earth is closest to the Sun during its orbit. Currently the Earth is further from the Sun during the northern hemisphere's summer than in the winter. This warms winters and cools summers. The precession completes its cycle every 21,000 years. A third, weaker cycle, with a return period of 100,000 years, alters the shape of the orbit and its eccentricity, and amplifies or reduces the effect of the precession.

Milankovitch predicted that the 21,000- and 41,000-year cycles could help cause ice ages by beginning a build-up of ice at the poles. They did this, he said, by making summers cooler, so that the winter's growth of snow and ice could not melt before the following winter's falls began. Milankovitch's ideas were developed in the 1970s by American scientists such as William Ruddiman and Andrew McIntyre of the Lamont-Doherty Geological Observatory. They argued that the Milankovitch wobbles were too small to create ice ages on their own and looked for an 'amplifier' for the weak Milankovitch signal. They settled on ice. Extra ice formed at the start of an ice age would, they said, increase the reflectivity of the planet, so cooling the planet further, setting up a positive feedback which would create the massive ice sheets characterizing the ice ages. It is the ice-albedo feedback predicted for our own greenhouse effect, but working in reverse.

Investigation of ice cores and sea sediments since 1970 have proved Milankovitch right in predicting that his cycles would influence temperatures. But they have raised many new questions about the mechanisms involved. The ice ages of the past million years have a frequency of 100,000 years. This is related to the third and weakest of the orbital cycles. Milankovitch did not predict this, and it remains a topic of hot debate.

Ruddiman and McIntyre developed the idea that the 100,000-year cycle dominates because it coincides with the time it takes ice sheets to grow to their maximum sustainable size. The idea is that as the world cooled, ice sheets grew, sea levels fell, and rainfall (or rather snowfall) would diminish until the ice sheets stopped growing. Eventually, when Milankovitch's wobbles moved into the right phase, strengthening the Sun in summer, more ice would melt in summer than accumulated in winter. The ice sheets would then start to disintegrate and, with reflectivity reduced, the planet would quickly warm again.

Physicists were very pleased with this theory. But during the 1980s biologists and chemists sought a slice of the action. They argued that if the physicists were right, the ice should melt before the planet warmed. Since ice melts slowly, this implied that warming would be slow. But research during the 1980s has repeatedly shown that at the end of the ice age, temperatures rose suddenly. The ice melted afterwards. The biologists therefore looked for other methods of amplifying the Milankovitch wobbles which could plunge the planet into and out of ice ages more swiftly.

These thoughts took two main lines. One stresses the ocean circulation system; the other stresses biological activity in the oceans. Both hinge on the close relationship between global temperatures and carbon dioxide, and the power of the ocean to draw carbon dioxide out of the atmosphere and to release it again. Some researchers still see the Milankovitch wobbles as essential to the ice age cycles; others would agree with Barry Saltzman and Kirk Maasch of Yale University that 'the carbon cycle can provide the instability necessary to drive major climatic variability without external forcing.' Either way, the implications could be profound. Humans may not be able to interfere with Milankovitch's planetary cycles, but we can certainly upset the carbon cycle.

First, we need to look at how the oceans work and how they influence the chemistry of the atmosphere — and hence climate.

COLD AND DEEP

The waters of the northern Atlantic Ocean are warm but deadly. This is where the Gulf Stream, flowing north from the tropics, meets the cold winds and icebergs of the Arctic. Trawlers caught in violent storms frequently disappear. A few pieces of wood or an occasional body may bob to the surface, but often they disappear without trace. This Bermuda Triangle of the north is, for oceanographers, one of the most important places on Earth. It is where the Gulf Stream suddenly turns turtle and dives to the bottom of the ocean. The far northern Atlantic is, in the language of oceanographers, where 'deep waters' form. It is the driving force for a stirring of the oceans which helps to control the climate of the planet. If there is one place which controls the planet's thermostat, it could be here in the stormy waters around Norway, Iceland and Greenland.

If there is a second, it is the ice-covered Weddell Sea, close to Antarctica. The antics of the water here are, if anything, even more extraordinary. Water from the deep rushes to the surface in the Weddell Sea, gives up huge amounts of heat and disappears to the bottom again. It does this, moreover, at particular spots where giant holes open up from time to time in the shelves of ice which cover the sea in winter. These holes are called 'polynyas'. Nobody knew they existed until satellites revealed them.

The most spectacular polynya was spotted on photographs taken by satellite in the winter of 1974. An area of sea, measuring up to 1,000 kilometres across, opened up in the midst of the winter ice. In that area of the sea, the ice melts in summer yet, the following winter, the gaping hole returned. It did the same in 1976, but disappeared in 1977. Measurements of heat given off by the ocean here show that, even when the hole is gone, the site of the polynya is where the greatest upwelling of deep waters around Antarctica takes place. It is where the deep waters of the ocean come up for air.

Oceans cover three-quarters of the Earth's surface. They are typically four kilometres deep and are made up of two layers. The top kilometre of water is the mixing layer: the water here is warmed by the Sun and travels the globe driven by the winds; this is the ocean that seafarers know. Beneath it there is another world that contains three-quarters of all the water in the oceans. It is a vast, cold and dense reservoir. Almost all the water in it, even at the equator, is colder than 4°C.

Water in the upper layer is in close touch with the air. It spends about a decade in the ocean before it evaporates or joins the deep circulation. The deep ocean is different. It is largely cut off from the atmosphere. Most of the water there is rising slowly towards the surface. This water is replaced by water plunging to the depths in just two places round the world, the far north Atlantic and the Weddell Sea. The chemical composition and temperature of the upper layer of the ocean reflect the state of the air above. The chemistry of water in the deep ocean reflects conditions when the water took its plunge to the depths. That could be a long time ago, since the deep water takes on average a thousand years to circulate through the ocean.

In the far north Atlantic, twenty million cubic metres of

water descend to the bottom of the ocean every second. This is more than a cubic kilometre every minute. In the Weddell Sea, the production of deep water is about half as much. These two places are where the deep ocean 'breathes', where its supply of oxygen and other chemicals is renewed. The north Atlantic may swallow up several billion tonnes of carbon dioxide each year in this way.

Nobody knows whether the Weddell Sea consumes or offers up carbon dioxide. Graham Chittleborough from the Australian government's Antarctic Division believes that the Weddell Sea removes up to two billion tonnes of carbon from the atmosphere each year. But most of the water that plunges to the bottom there seems to be recycled deep water which has risen to the surface in polynyas. So it is equally likely that the surfacing water releases into the air more than it grabs. What is certain is that events in these two small patches of ocean are important in determining how much carbon dioxide the ocean can absorb. The deep ocean circulation can 'bury' carbon in the ocean for a thousand years. Any change in climate or biological activity in these areas could drastically influence the operation of the deep ocean's 'lungs' and alter the progress of greenhouse warming.

In the past few years, geochemists such as Wally Broecker and his colleagues at the Lamont-Doherty Geological Observatory have plotted the course of the deep-water circulation along the bottom of the oceans. The main stream, beginning in the far north Atlantic, travels south, flowing deep beneath the path of the Gulf Stream as far as the Southern Ocean. It carries more than twenty times as much water as all the world's rivers. In the Southern Ocean, part of the current carries on south to take a gulp of air in the Weddell Sea, but most rounds the Cape of Good Hope, the southern tip of Africa, and spreads out into the Indian and Pacific Oceans. In the north Pacific it turns, rising towards the surface and gathering heat, before eventually making its way back to the Atlantic and the Gulf Stream to start the cycle again.

Why does the warm Gulf Stream suddenly plunge to the depths? The cause is its sudden meeting with Arctic winds and ice. The bitter winds blowing off Greenland and Canada evaporate moisture from the Gulf Stream. More water is frozen to form part of the Arctic ice pack. Both processes remove fresh water, so what is left is unusually saline. Salty water is dense water. Dense water sinks and here it is dense enough to sink to the bottom.

There is no obvious reason why deep water should not form in the north Pacific rather than the Atlantic. Some researchers think it once did. We have 'a classic chicken and egg situation', says Broecker. Because the north Atlantic is warmer than the north Pacific, more water evaporates, making what remains denser so that it takes its dive and continues the circulation. That circulation sustains the warmth of the north Atlantic. 'Excess evaporation causes the deep current; the deep current causes excess evaporation,' says Broecker. He guesses that the balance of salt in the oceans is maintained when the fresh water that evaporates from the Atlantic falls as rain in the north Pacific, where it keeps that ocean fresh and buoyant.

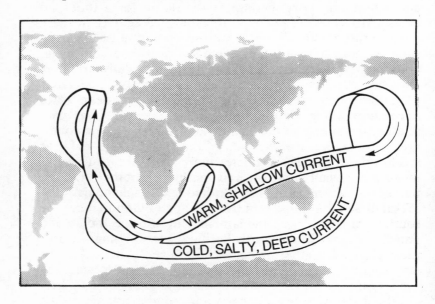

The deep-ocean circulation. It carries twenty times more water than all of the world's rivers, and helps to keep Europe warm.

How fickle is this circulation? There is growing evidence, say Nicholas Shackleton from the University of Cambridge and a French co-author, Jean-Claude Duplessy, that 'the circulation of the world ocean deep water is very sensitive to climate and that it changes drastically during climatic transitions.' It is one likely mechanism by which the planet lurches into and out of ice ages. We shall return to it. The second likely mechanism is the 'biological pump'.

THE BIOLOGICAL PUMP

The phrase 'biological pump' was coined by Roger Revelle when he was at the Scripps Institution of Oceanography in California. The idea it encapsulates has become a cornerstone of discussion about the impact of life on the Earth's atmosphere and probably goes a long way to explaining the onset of the ice ages. The pump is the means by which life in the oceans draws carbon dioxide from the air to the ocean and dispatches it from the surface layers of the ocean to the depths.

All living organisms require a few basic chemicals to survive. The most critical elements for life in the ocean appear to be carbon and two nutrients, nitrogen and phosphorus. In the modern world, biological tissue requires these chemicals in a fixed ratio known, after the discoverer of the ratio, Arthur Redfield, as the 'Redfield ratios'. One atom of phosphorus is required for every 15 atoms of nitrogen and every 105 atoms of carbon.

With carbon readily replenished from the atmosphere, the limiting factor for the growth of marine organisms is usually the nutrients, especially phosphorus. The only exception seems to be the far northern and southern latitudes, where a lack of sunlight in winter has been widely assumed to limit growth. (As we shall see later, however, a new theory, which identifies a shortage of iron as critical, may have important implications for theories about the onset of ice ages.)

Most of the nitrogen and phosphorus in the ocean is in the deep-water layer and is delivered to the surface waters by the deep-ocean circulation. In the surface waters, the nutrients meet carbon and light, and create living organisms. Today,

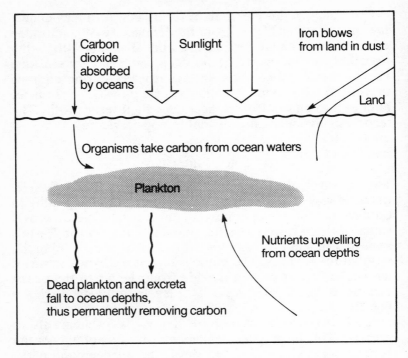

The 'biological pump'. In most places the supply of nutrients limits the growth of plankton — and hence the ability of marine organisms to absorb carbon dioxide from the air.

about half of the nutrients in this deep ocean reservoir come from the decomposition of organisms falling from the sea above. The rest is brought down from the surface directly by the formation of deep water. This second supply comes partly from chemicals washed from the land, but mainly from nutrients left over from the previous meeting of carbon and nutrients in the surface waters. This means that biological activity in the waters close to the Arctic and Antarctic may be critical to the efficient operation of the pump. These waters provide the last chance for nutrients to be used up before disappearing to the ocean deep. They are also the places where nitrogen and phosphorus are most likely not to be used up, because of shortages of sunlight and, it seems, iron.

One measure of the efficiency of the biological pump is the amount of nutrients left over from each circulation of the ocean. An efficient pump uses up all the nutrients to maximize the drawdown of carbon dioxide. But the ability of the pump to extract carbon dioxide from the air also depends on how much nutrient reaches the oceans from the land, and on the speed of the ocean circulation.

During the ice ages, the biological pump worked with great efficiency, drawing carbon from the atmosphere deep into the ocean. The amount of carbon dioxide in the air fell exactly as temperatures fell. One recent study concluded it was possible that a variation in the amount of 'leftover' nutrient could account for a swing in the amount of carbon dioxide in the air of around 100 ppm. This is strikingly similar to the range of values seen between ice ages and interglacial periods.

Why was the biological pump more efficient during the ice ages? The evidence here is confusing. For instance, the ocean circulation was probably more sluggish then. But it is not clear whether that would have reduced the amount of nutrients upwelling from the deep ocean or ensured that a greater proportion of the nutrients was used up in the surface waters. The former would warm the planet; the latter would cool it.

Michael McElroy from Harvard has developed an idea suggested in the early 1980s by, among others, Broecker. The notion is that during the ice ages there was a substantial increase in the amount of nutrients reaching the oceans from the land. He says that the nutrient in shortest supply would probably have been phosphorus, supplied primarily by the erosion of phosphate beds on land. When phosphorus is washed into the sea by rivers, some joins the ocean circulation and some falls swiftly to the bottoms of the wide shallow seas that cover the continental shelves surrounding the continents. The phosphorus that joins the ocean circulation can feed the biological pump. The phosphorus that drops on to the shelves is lost to the system. Today, the giant alluvial fans, which extend into the sea from the mouths of big rivers such as the River Amazon, are one example of the kinds of places that could harbour phosphates.

McElroy's reasoning is that the proportion of phosphorus that joins the ocean circulation may vary greatly, depending on sea levels. The sea level in turn depends on the temperature of the atmosphere. When the world is warm, the ice caps start to melt and seas are high. The submerged continental shelves are wide and a lot of phosphorus is trapped there. When the world cools, more water is held in ice caps and seas are low. The shelves are exposed and eroded. Rivers wash the phosphorus into the oceans, where it is almost all caught up in the ocean circulation. The phosphorus fuels the biological pump, sending it into a higher gear. The pump draws down carbon dioxide from the air, cooling the atmosphere further. This positive feedback turns what might have been a small cooling, caused perhaps by the 100,000-year Milankovitch wobble, into an ice age.

What might end the ice age? McElroy speculates that, with a biological pump going at full pelt, the life in the oceans would use up vast amounts of oxygen. A sluggish deep-ocean circulation would, if anything, drag less oxygen into the ocean depths. So, says McElroy, 'eventually, the productivity of the ocean would rise to the point where the supply of oxygen was inadequate to keep pace.' When the oxygen runs out, marine organisms would die, dumping phosphates on to the sea bed. The biological pump falters and carbon dioxide bubbles back into the air, warming the planet. Ice would then melt. Sea levels would rise and the nutrients would again go into store on the continental shelves. Thus a positive feedback would be bringing the ice age to a close.

It is a compelling idea. McElroy points out that current estimates show that phosphorus washed from the land typically spends about 100,000 years in the ocean, taking part in life in the surface layers, floating down to be captured by the deep circulation and being brought back up to help form new life many times over before finally falling to the sea floor. He believes that the coincidence of the 100,000-year cycle could be a strong indication that the cycling of phosphorus into and out of the ocean is a central feature in the 100,000-year oscillation of the ice ages.

Much of the early work developing the notion that the

146

efficiency of the biological pump switched the planet into and out of ice ages was done by Wally Broecker. But in the mid-1980s, he changed his mind. He began to think that the events at the end of the ice ages were too sudden to be explained by changes in sea levels. The end of the ice age was characterized by sudden lurches, lasting only around 100 years, in both temperatures and the amount of carbon dioxide in the air. The timescales involved in the nutrient cycling seem much too slow to cause such abrupt changes. And sea levels do not change overnight. At the end of the last ice age, 50 million cubic kilometres of ice melted, but it took several thousand years.

Broecker is firm about the failings of his first idea. 'If these [abrupt] carbon dioxide changes are typical of the atmosphere,' he says, 'the explanations involving the transfer of nutrient substances between the ocean and its shelf sediments must be abandoned. Such transfers could certainly not occur fast enough to produce 60 ppm carbon dioxide changes in a hundred years.'

The timing of events also appears to be wrong. Analyses of the Vostok ice cores suggest that, at the end of the most recent ice age, carbon dioxide levels increased before the sea levels rose. In McElroy's scenario the sea level would have to change first. By 1987 Broecker was saying that 'the only feasible mechanism scientists have come up with to explain rapid changes in the atmosphere's carbon dioxide content involves modifications in the ocean's circulation pattern and intensity.'

THE TWO-MODE WORLD WITH IRON IN ITS SOUL

Broecker says we must throw out all the old ideas about gradual change between ice ages and interglacials. There are, he says, two 'stable modes of operation' for the oceans and atmosphere. Up to now, one has accompanied ice ages, the other interglacials. During interglacials, such as the present one, there is a very active deep-ocean circulation with lots of deep water formed in the northern Atlantic. During ice ages, no deep water is formed in the north Atlantic and the circulation slows. Broecker believes that

147

the planet flips between the two stable modes almost as fast, in geological terms, as the winds swing round at the beginning and end of monsoons.

The most intriguing evidence about these flips between modes comes from the quite unexpected discovery in pollen remains in European bogs of a sudden climatic flip 11,000 years ago. For 2,000 years the world had raced out of the last ice age, with glaciers and ice caps melting round the world and the deep-ocean circulation going full pelt. Trees had returned to most of Europe, replacing the grass and scrub of the ice age tundra. Then, quite abruptly, the trees disappeared again. The ice age resumed for 800 years, during which time carbon dioxide levels in the atmosphere fell by about a quarter. Pack ice floated down the west coast of Europe as far as Spain. Then, 10,200 years ago, temperatures and carbon dioxide levels rose once more, and forests returned to Europe.

Broecker argues that the only plausible explanation for this sudden reverse, known as the 'Younger-Dryas Period', is that the Gulf Stream shut down for those 800 years. The Gulf Stream today dominates the climate of western Europe. The reason is the staggering amount of heat that it gives off. The stream arrives in the region with a temperature of about 10°C but leaves, plunging to the depths, at a temperature of about 2°C. That heat warms the cold winds blowing across the current, travelling west to Europe. The heat released is equal to around 30% of the solar heat reaching the surface of the ocean at these latitudes. It keeps Siberian weather away from most of western Europe and ensures, for instance, that London remains many degrees warmer in winter than New York, even though London is 1,000 kilometres further north. Broecker says that if the Gulf Stream shut down today it 'would cool the north Atlantic and its adjacent lands by 6 to 8°C.'

His explanation for the closing of the ice age and for why the Gulf Stream shut down for those 800 years goes like this. The trigger for the end of the ice age was a small Milankovitch wobble which warmed northern latitudes in summer. This increased evaporation in the north Atlantic, creating a build-up of salt and the resumption of the formation of deep water. The evaporation also released heat, which began to melt ice.

The melting of ice caps takes a long time to get going, creating a destabilizing timelag. The atmosphere is warm but the ice caps persist. One of the largest ice sheets covered the Laurentian shield, centred on the Great Lakes of North America. At first, the millions of cubic kilometres of melting water from this sheet flowed south into the Mississippi and the Gulf of Mexico. But once the sheet had retreated far enough, Broecker speculates, it would probably quite suddenly have begun to drain into the St Lawrence River and the north Atlantic. This is the route that the water from today's Great Lakes takes to the sea. A sudden massive influx of fresh water into the north Atlantic would have drastically reduced the saltiness of the sea. Less salt meant the water was less dense. That, says Broecker, meant 'significantly reduced deep-water production, returning northern Atlantic climates to their glacial state'. The hold-up to the global warming was temporary. The cold weather halted the melting of ice and allowed the build-up of salt in the northern Atlantic to resume.

This theory leaves many questions unanswered. There is growing evidence that the formation of deep water in the far northern Atlantic did shut down during the ice age. Most deep water at that time seems to have been formed in the waters around the Antarctic. But it is far from clear why that should have so drastically altered the operation of the biological pump. Indeed there is a good case for arguing that a shut-down circulation ought to have shut down the biological pump as well, which should have warmed the planet rather than cooling it. There seemed to be a missing ingredient.

In 1988 scientists became excited by an idea that seemed to offer just such an ingredient: iron. John Martin and Steve Fitzwater, from the Moss Landing Marine Laboratories in California, began by questioning whether a shortage of sunlight was the true cause of the poor uptake of nutrients by sea life in Arctic and Antarctic waters. Playing a hunch, they sampled water from the cold Alaskan Gulf in the far north-east of the Pacific Ocean. They found that only a quarter of the available nitrogen in the water was used up by plankton there. Back in the laboratory, they fed the plankton some iron and there was 'nearly complete utilization' of the nitrogen.

It is well enough known among biologists that iron is essential to life. But nobody had thought before that it might be an ingredient in short supply. The finding shows that, in the kind of polar waters where the inefficiencies of the biological pump are most marked today, iron can have a dramatic effect in improving the efficiency of the pump. As the authors put it: 'Oceanic iron availability may be important in determining global atmospheric carbon dioxide levels, and hence affecting global climate.'

Iron reaches the oceans almost entirely from land. It blows across the oceans in dust. If the iron gives out, say Martin and Fitzwater, then so does life in the oceans. Today the shortage of iron is probably most acute around the Antarctic, where possible sources of dust are thousands of kilometres away. 'We postulate that iron supplies from local Antarctic continental margin sources are rapidly used up in the highly productive waters of this region and little, if any, mixes out into the Southern Ocean.' But — and here is the link to climate change — it is widely agreed that during the ice ages there was between ten and twenty times more dust in the atmosphere than today. This is because the tropical deserts, which are the main source of dust, were five times larger then, and wind speeds are generally supposed to have been higher. 'We postulate,' say Martin and Fitzwater, 'that the enhanced supply of iron from the atmosphere [during the ice ages] stimulated photosynthesis, which led to the drawdown in atmospheric carbon dioxide levels during the glacial maxima.'

The idea has caused great excitement. The feedback is strong and could operate very quickly, because it is independent of the deep-ocean circulation and does not rely on rising or falling sea levels. The researchers would like to test it out by spraying iron dust on to a patch of the Alaskan Gulf to see if plankton proliferate. We might already be providing a global experiment with the spreading of deserts. The dust storms blowing out of Africa could be helping to keep temperatures down. And if they are not, as my colleague John Gribbin suggested in a letter to *Nature*, 'by adding iron compounds to the oceans, a "technological fix" to remove carbon dioxide from the air might be practicable.'

THE SUPER-INTERGLACIAL

During the 1990s, oceanography seems set to become one of the most important disciplines in the search for the keys to the global thermostat. Data from the Vostok ice core has provided plenty of clues, and reinforced the view that somewhere in the relationship between ocean circulation and the efficiency of the biological pump in the oceans lies the true cause of the ice ages.

That truth is of more than academic interest. The evidence is growing that the ocean is a temperamental controller of our climate. Small changes in the atmosphere may trigger large shifts in the circulation and biology of the oceans, which in turn cause large-scale climatic shifts. We need to know swiftly whether the greenhouse effect being perpetrated by our own recent activities has the potential to cause changes that could be far in excess and far more abrupt than those predicted by climate modellers.

Today, after 10,000 years of relative calm in this hair-trigger climatic system, humans are pumping so much carbon dioxide and other greenhouse gases into the air and chopping down so many trees that we might trigger another lurch in the system. But what, as we enter the uncharted waters of the 'super-interglacial' era, might that lurch be? 'What is the likelihood,' Broecker asks, 'that increases in carbon dioxide and other greenhouse gases will jolt the ocean-atmosphere system out of its current mode?' If we switch off the deep-ocean circulation, will we escalate the global warming? Might we dump ourselves back into the ice ages? We have little idea what lies in the active chamber of the gun as we play Russian roulette with our climate.

Barrie Hunt, Australia's veteran climatic modeller, joins Broecker in worrying that after twenty years of research into the greenhouse effect, we have seven or eight laboratories doing models. They all show the same things. We should be thinking about the more fundamental problems about the greenhouse. Why shouldn't there be a new Younger Dryas?

For a further insight into what might happen, I went to James McCarthy at Harvard, the chairman of the International Geosphere-Biosphere Programme. He is worried about the impact of a greenhouse warming on northern polar air in winter. That air will become much warmer than today, and so will the surface layers of northern waters. The differences in temperature between the Arctic waters and the incoming Gulf Stream could diminish by several degrees. That, McCarthy says, would slow the formation of deep waters in the far north Atlantic. This water is a 'major pathway' for the input to the deep sea of nutrients, the fuel for the biological pump. So, if the deep-water circulation slows, there could be a partial shutdown of the biological pump, he says. This would increase the carbon dioxide in the air, intensifying the greenhouse warming. 'In an extreme situation,' says McCarthy, 'the warming might shut down deep-water formation altogether in the north Atlantic.' We would have broken the global thermostat.

Is anything of the sort starting to happen? In December 1983, Broecker and his colleague at Columbia, Taro Takahashi, reported a freshening of the waters of the far north Atlantic over the previous twenty years. From the Labrador Sea between Greenland and Canada to the waters between Scotland and Iceland, the water was found to be less salty and less dense than in the late 1950s. 'The broad scope of this deep freshening suggests a linkage with a larger-scale climatic change,' they said. But what is the linkage? Will it feed on itself? Is it connected to the intriguing discovery that waves were about 25% bigger throughout the north Atlantic in the 1980s than in the 1960s? Is it the first sign of McCarthy's slowdown of the biological pump and the deep-ocean circulation? For the moment, nobody knows. McCarthy believes it is imperative to find out.

The Causes of Ice Ages

A thorough investigation of the operation of the biological pump will also have to look at how we may feed it by polluting the oceans with chemicals. Already, our handiwork may be evident on a wider scale than usually admitted.

MORE BLOOMING TROUBLE

1987 was the year of the 'red tides', floating masses of algae washing up on the seashore. Many of them were toxic, though not all of them, strictly speaking, red. The US had seen nothing like it before. Late in August, the algae began forming first off Naples in Florida. Two months later, the *New York Times* reported a red tide along much of the coast of North Carolina. The organism, *Ptychodiscus brevis*, 'turned the waters yellow, devastating fishing and tourist economies,' said the paper. It caused a variety of illnesses among people working in the water or spending time on the beaches, the paper reported. 'We are seeing global change,' said Theodore Smayda, a professor at the University of Rhode Island, as red tides appeared there, too. The fear was that humans were interfering with the biological pump in a rather direct way, by feeding algae, one of its most important operatives.

That summer, reports of red tides came in from Hong Kong, Guatemala, Tasmania, Taiwan, South Korea and Venezuela. Many places treated the tides as an odd local phenomenon. It was only when the reports were assembled that the scale of what appeared to be going on emerged.

The growth of thick mats of algae on the waters of oceans and estuaries is no recent phenomenon. But the evidence is growing that there are more red tides and algal blooms than there used to be. It is hard to be certain, however. People may just be looking harder. Scientists once thought that blooms were confined to estuaries and coastal waters, but satellite pictures show that every spring great blooms of algae spread across much of the far north Atlantic. Have they always been there? Waters where blooms proliferate include those close to the Arctic ice pack where the deep waters form and the biological pump is at its most vulnerable. The North Sea, which is largely surrounded by land, is one

153

of the most algae-infested areas in the Atlantic area. Blooms there appear to be increasing in frequency. One bloom in the Skagerrak, the water between Denmark and Norway that links the Baltic and North seas, caused a panic in Scandinavia in May 1988 when it killed fish and threatened fish farms on the Norwegian coast.

Blooms form when there is an excess of nutrients reaching the surface waters, either upwelling from ocean depths or running into the seas from rivers. In the polar waters, nutrients build up in winter and there is a surge in algae growth in spring. The conventional view is that this happens because algae bask in the spring Sun and gobble up the reservoir of food in their waters. But the discoveries by Martin and Fitzwater about the role of iron in stimulating plankton in these waters suggests that there may be more to it than that.

Most of the time, most of the carbon dissolved into the surface layers of the ocean and eaten by algae is recycled repeatedly through other organisms. It passes through many bodies before it finally falls out of the surface waters and on to the ocean floor. But when blooms form, much more of their remains passes quickly to the bottom. They overwhelm the recycling system. Blooms, says McCarthy at Harvard, could have a quite disproportionate role in the efficiency of the operation of the biological pump. They represent the pump in overdrive. 'Variations in the rates of algal production . . . in these regions can substantially alter partitioning of carbon, with consequences of global significance . . . including [for] concentrations of atmospheric carbon dioxide,' he says.

Marine biologists are desperately ignorant about how much carbon there is in the oceans and what it is doing. They used to think most of the carbon was inorganic. But, in 1988, a study by two Japanese researchers, Yukio Sugimura and Yoshimi Suzuki of the Meteorological Research Institute in Tsukuba, forced researchers to quadruple their estimates of how much dissolved organic carbon there is in the surface waters. This dissolved organic carbon is partly organic material washed into the sea by rivers, but is largely made up of the bodily remains of living marine organisms. It is also, of course, a prime source of food for other marine organisms.

The new numbers seem to make more sense than the old ones when plugged into models of global carbon circulation. There had been a 'missing carbon' problem in the ocean similar to that on land.

Dissolved organic material is, in effect, a kind of floating, very dilute oceanic soil, taking part in all manner of chemical reactions, sustaining life and forming one of the least understood carbon reservoirs in the living parts of the planet.

Plants in the oceans have a much faster metabolism than plants on land. At any one time there is around 100 times more carbon stored in the biomass on land than there is in the oceans. Yet the rate of photosynthesis, the turnover of carbon, is roughly the same in both worlds. While trees and other land plants put carbon into leaves, stems and roots, the algae that dominate the oceans float freely on the waters and have little need for such superstructures. They invest most of their carbon in proteins and simple sugars, i.e. in energy to grow and procreate. While trees take decades to grow, many marine phytoplankton double their size in a day or so. If nitrogen or phosphorus fertilizer is spread on to a field or forest, a response can be expected over months or years. Pour them on to the ocean and a very significant response will be seen overnight.

The worry is that this is precisely what we are doing to create the new virulent algal blooms and red tides. We may be overfertilizing the oceans, especially the coastal waters. Our fertilizing pollution comes in nitrogen and phosphorus fertilizers put on to fields and later washed into rivers and the sea. It also comes in sewage, which is packed full of nutrients that algae love to eat. When the Skagerrak algal bloom was at its height in May 1988, the concentration of nitrogen from sewage flowing into the sea from the River Elbe and others appeared to be unusually high.

There are other sources, too. On the east coast of the US and in Europe nitrogen from car exhausts, falling into estuaries and the oceans, could be an important ingredient. A study published in early 1988 by the US's Natural Environment Defense Fund found that most of the nutrients in Chesapeake Bay, the largest estuary in the US, came from air pollution. Katharine Lam from the Hong Kong Environmental Protection Agency claims to have found a correlation between areas of the sea around Hong Kong that are most polluted with sewage and those afflicted by red tides. As Bert Bolin, one of the senior figures in the debates about global change, observed: 'It is difficult to identify a major river or estuary that has not been affected by the addition of phosphate from agricultural or industrial sources.'

What effect would fertilizing the oceans have? Two British investigators, Peter Liss and Andy Crane, observed in 1983, 'the resulting enhanced production and subsequent sedimentation might contribute a valid route for uptake of additional carbon dioxide by the marine environment.' In other words, by sprinkling the oceans liberally with fertilizers, we might speed up the biological pump, so eating up some of the carbon dioxide we have put into the air and helping to reduce the greenhouse effect.

10
GREENHOUSE COCKTAIL

The exhaust fumes from motor cars and the farts from cattle have formed a disturbing chemical alliance. The increase in the numbers of cattle and cars in almost every country in the world threatens to do as much to advance the greenhouse effect as carbon dioxide from power stations. And the chemical cocktail they are creating in the atmosphere may turn out to be an essential ingredient in the creation of the ozone hole and the spread of acid rain.

Human activities in the past century have produced a big increase in the atmospheric concentrations of several greenhouse gases besides carbon dioxide. Paddy fields and waste tips, coal mines and farm fertilizers all play their part. But we start with farting cattle and their contribution to the atmosphere: prodigious quantities of methane.

The cattle population of the world rose from 700 million animals in 1940 to 1,300 million in the mid-1980s, i.e. about one cow for every four people. A typical cow eats four kilograms of food per day. The bacteria in the guts of cattle gobble up this food and convert anywhere between 5 and 10% of it into methane, which the cows expel into the air through one orifice or another. All herbivores, including wild animals such as elephants and giraffes, produce methane. But the combined emissions from the wild are small today, compared with domesticated animals.

Our knowledge of methane's place in the world has come a long way since its association with marsh gas and explosions

157

in coal mines. It is now a key ingredient in the complex atmospheric soup that we are creating above our heads. The methane molecule comprises one atom of carbon and four of hydrogen. Methane is a greenhouse gas second only to carbon dioxide in its importance in heating up the atmosphere. It has already doubled its concentration since pre-industrial times. Levels rose by 1% a year during the 1980s. Bubbles of ancient air inside the ice packs of Greenland and Antarctica show that today's level of about 1.7 ppm is five times that during the last ice age.

Working out how much methane the world's cattle fart and belch into the air is a hard task. Dieter Ehhalt, from the Max Planck Institute of Atmospheric Chemistry in West Germany, reckons the bacteria inside a typical cow produce about 200 grams of methane a day. Multiply that by the world's cattle population and you have 90 million tonnes of methane a year.

Besides the guts of cows, other happy oxygen-free homes for methane-producing microbes include swamps and marshes, hence methane's popular name of marsh gas. Humans have drained many of these wetlands (210,000 square kilometres in Europe alone, according to one estimate). But many more survive, from the flood plains of the Amazon to the papyrus swamps of East Africa and the frozen bogs, or tundras, of northern Canada and Siberia.

Humans have replaced natural marshes with a mimic — rice paddy fields, where methane-producing microbes thrive. Ehhalt puts the output of methane from rice fields at 50 million tonnes per year, roughly the same as that from surviving swamps. Coal and natural gas are the remains of ancient bogs; coal mines and natural gas pipelines both give off methane.

In the tundra, methane is trapped in ice, ready for release as global warming melts the frozen subsoils. There are also large stores of methane trapped inside ice structures in sediments on ocean floors. The bed of the Arctic Ocean contains these 'methane hydrates', so too may some deep ocean troughs. The low temperatures and high pressures on the sea bed keep the shells of the hydrates frozen. But if the shell cracks large amounts of methane can be released.

158

Russian researchers claim to have measured methane and other gases rushing to the surface of the ocean from cracks in the methane hydrates in the Sea of Okhotsk on the eastern shores of Siberia. They also claim to have found methane hydrates in the Bermuda trough in the Atlantic Ocean. The Soviet science magazine *Priroda* speculated that gases from the rocks might overwhelm people on board ships or low-flying aircraft, thus explaining the strange goings on in the Bermuda Triangle!

Methane hydrates may already be the most important source of methane in the atmosphere. Some 150 million tonnes a year is one guesstimate. Investigators wonder whether a greenhouse warming might unlock much more methane from hydrates beneath the oceans and tundras on land. The methane would accelerate the warming, setting up a nasty positive feedback.

Outstripping all other known sources of methane may be the guts of termites. In 1982 scientists from the US, Kenya and West Germany published a study of American termites. They had collected the termites in small boxes placed beneath rocks in Colorado and from cow dung in the pastures of Arizona. Back in the laboratory, they fed the bugs and observed their excretions. The researchers found that bacteria in the termites' guts converted most of the carbon in the termites' food into the greenhouse gases carbon dioxide and methane.

One termite may not do much harm. But the world has an estimated 250 million billion termites. They may be best known for creating outsize termite mounds (the world's largest, in Australia, is about six metres high). But, less ostentatiously, they occupy two-thirds of the world's land area and eat approaching a third of all the world's vege-tation. They live in greatest profusion in tropical grasslands and pastures, just the kind of environment being created by the destruction of tropical rainforests. The study concluded that annual emissions of methane from termites could amount to 150 million tonnes.

One of the authors of that paper was Paul Crutzen, one of Ehhalt's colleagues. He put his name, two years later, to a claim that modern urban waste dumps are a major new source of methane. Waste tips contain lots of organic materials, from old food to paper packaging, slowly putrefying in an oxygen-free environment. Bugs love tips and generate lots of methane in them. In Britain, several tips have leaked their gases into the basements of houses. Sometimes the methane ignites. In March 1986 in the Derbyshire village of Loscoe, methane from an old tip turned a bungalow into a heap of rubble. Two years later, government inspectors revealed that there were risks of methane explosions near some 1,300 waste tips. Modern wastes and modern techniques of squashing waste on tips to get more in have drastically increased methane production.

Crutzen argues that 'very large increases in methane production from waste dumps are expected in the coming decades from the developing world. Consequently, methane production from municipal and industrial wastes could become one of the main contributors to the global atmospheric methane budget.' He reckoned production could already be up to 70 million tonnes a year.

Almost every month new and surprising ideas about the formation of methane turn up in the scientific press. Natural gas leaking from pipelines and deliberately vented from oil and gas wells could be a large source — probably larger today than coal mines. So, according to William Sachett and Timothy Barber of the University of South Florida, could asphalt. Sunlight on a hot asphalt road or roof produces chemical reactions which liberate a slow but steady supply of methane into the air — up to five million tonnes a year in the US alone, according to the researchers.

Humans are having a big influence on sources of methane in the atmosphere, whether by creating nice environments for termites, by breeding more cattle, by digging rice paddies, by spreading asphalt or by dumping municipal trash. Each year about 50 million tonnes more methane enters the atmosphere than leaves it. But its lifetime in the atmosphere, currently about ten years, is probably increasing. Humans may be having as drastic an effect on the 'sinks' for methane as on the sources. And this spells more trouble.

Greenhouse Cocktail

CARS, COWS AND THE PLANETARY CLEANSING SERVICE

There are several hundred million motor cars in the world. They are proliferating even faster than cattle. In some countries, such as West Germany, there is one car for every two people. The chemicals that pour from car exhausts are the most pervasive form of pollution in the world. They are nitrogen oxides, various hydrocarbons and carbon monoxide.

Nitrogen oxides often turn to nitric acid in the atmosphere and fall to the ground as acid rain. Car exhausts are the biggest source of acid rain in the most prosperous countries of Europe and in the US. In sunlight, nitrogen oxides will also combine with hydrocarbons from car exhausts, chemical works and natural sources such as trees to form a photochemical smog of the kind first made famous in Los Angeles in the 1940s. These smogs build up during hot, sunny weather. They generate heat haze, and can drift for thousands of kilometres. The smogs contain ozone, which damages plants, decomposes everything from condoms to furnishings, and causes both premature ageing of lungs and attacks of asthma in humans.

Carbon monoxide, the third pollutant from cars, is a destructive force in the complex chemistry that stops the atmosphere cleansing itself of pollutants, including methane. Over half of the carbon monoxide put into the atmosphere each year comes from human activities. One recent estimate is that we are responsible for the emission of 1,500 million tonnes of it. Some is from tropical forests, one of the multitude of organic chemicals given off when trees are burned. Some is from the chemical breakdown of methane, but probably most comes from burning fossil fuels, especially petrol in the internal combustion engines of cars.

We have doubled the amount of carbon monoxide in the lower atmosphere in the past century or so to roughly 120 parts per billion (ppb). Concentrations are rising by between 1 and 2% each year, but by much more in industrial countries. Cape Meares is a remote rural spot in the US state of Oregon. It is one of the global network of monitors of 'background' levels of gases, yet it currently registers a 6% annual increase in carbon monoxide levels.

161

Carbon monoxide reacts easily with other chemicals in the air, so it does not spread as far round the world as, say, CFCs or carbon dioxide. However, this ready reactivity gives carbon monoxide a potent influence on other chemicals which do have a global range. Much the most important of these is hydroxyl, a naturally occurring chemical made up of one atom of oxygen and one of hydrogen. It is produced when ultraviolet radiation bombards ozone.

Hydroxyl is present in the atmosphere only at minute concentrations, roughly one part in 100 million million. It is one of a number of chemicals called 'free radicals', and it lives up to this name by causing chemical mayhem wherever it goes. There is twenty million million times more oxygen in the atmosphere than hydroxyl. Yet hydroxyl is more important than oxygen in oxidizing other chemicals by supplying oxygen atoms to them. This means that it sets the speed for oxidation, one of the key chemical operations of the atmosphere.

Jim Anderson from Harvard University, who takes a special interest in free radicals, says that hydroxyl removes many pollutants from the atmosphere. Its power to oxidize other chemicals makes it the cleansing agent for the atmosphere. It is therefore disconcerting to discover that the amount of hydroxyl in the air has begun to sag alarmingly, especially over the middle latitudes of the northern hemisphere. American investigators, such as Joel Levine at NASA's Langley Research Center, suggest that there is about a quarter less hydroxyl in these latitudes than there was 40 years ago.

One of hydroxyl's modern housekeeping duties is to trigger the conversion of the pollutant sulphur dioxide to sulphuric acid, which then falls to the ground as acid rain. The partial disappearance of hydroxyl could be one reason for the spread of acid rain away from the industrial areas of Europe and the US towards remote places such as the lakes of Canada and Scandinavia.

The most important reason for the decline of hydroxyl concentrations appears to be the growing amount of carbon monoxide in the air. (Carbon monoxide accounts for up to 80% of the destruction of hydroxyl.) The most important consequence of the decline of hydroxyl is probably the rising concentration of methane in the atmosphere.

In the natural world, there is a fine balancing act between carbon monoxide and methane. The balance is managed by hydroxyl. By filling the air with fumes from car exhausts, we have upset that balance. More carbon monoxide eats up hydroxyl. There is not enough left to restrain the large amounts of methane that we inflict on the atmosphere. Donald Blake of the University of California at Irvine sums up: 'The atmospheric concentrations of carbon monoxide, methane and the hydroxyl radical are all closely coupled with one another, and increasing concentrations of carbon monoxide and/or methane should cause reduced concentrations of hydroxyl, which in turn should lengthen the atmospheric lifetimes of carbon monoxide and methane.'

The enfeebling of the planetary cleansing service means that a vast range of gases, some natural and some man-made, also survive longer in the atmosphere. Anderson believes it is a much more important reason for the build-up of methane than any increase in output from cattle or paddy fields. There are other worrying consequences. CFCs, the greenhouse gases that double as deadly warriors against the ozone layer, last many decades, allowing them time to reach the ozone layer. Less hydroxyl mean that they last even longer, doing more damage to ozone and heating the planet further. Cars may have a lot to answer for.

There is another twist to the story. It turns out that methane is a menace to the ozone layer. It breaks down there, releasing hydrogen atoms that form water. The stratosphere is generally very dry, but clouds of frozen water vapour are more frequent in the stratosphere over the Antarctic today, and are seen occasionally over the Arctic. As we have seen, these stratospheric clouds are crucial to the formation of ozone holes. More methane means more clouds. As Blake told the American Chemical Society in 1987: 'An increase in stratospheric water vapour ... could contribute to further decreases in total ozone over Antarctica.'

Blake and Sherry Rowland (the guru of the ozone chemists) say that in the past 40 years, the amount of water in the stratosphere has risen by 28%. They say methane is responsible for most of this increase. And they have another point. Besides threatening the ozone layer, water in the stratosphere is a potent greenhouse gas. A doubling of water in the stratosphere has an effect equal to that of doubling carbon dioxide in the troposphere. Here is another link between the ozone hole and greenhouse warming. Stephen Schneider, the American climate modeller, warns that one effect of the greenhouse warming could be to encourage the updraught of methane into the stratosphere, perhaps through more and bigger tropical storm clouds. As the methane creates water vapour and the planet warms further, a potentially extremely dangerous positive feedback could be set in motion. This is a classic example of one of the scientific 'surprises' that people such as Schneider feel could make nonsense of the current climate models.

JEKYLL AND HYDE

The growing international concern about forms of air pollution that have an impact on the great global life-support systems has begun to dull interest in concerns of the early 1980s such as acid rain. Nonetheless, acid rain is an important international issue likely to hit the developing nations increasingly in the coming decades. In the past century, acid pollution has ceased to be a mere local intrusion — stopping trees growing on the Pennine hills of England, for instance. Since the 1960s it has been of international concern. Norway and Sweden have blamed Britain and other European nations for unleashing so much acid on winds heading for Scandinavia that thousands of lakes have become acid and lost their fish. Canada has made similar complaints about the US. The same acid, mostly sulphuric acid from the chimneys of power stations, has acidified soils across most of Europe. This has washed nutrients such as calcium from soils and liberated instead toxic metals such as aluminium. Aluminium kills fish in acid streams and is strongly implicated, along with direct assaults from air pollution and climatic extremes, in the sickness among Europe's trees.

There are two main forms of acid rain: sulphuric acid

created by sulphur dioxide unleashed when fossil fuels are burned in power stations; and nitric acid from both power stations and vehicle exhausts. In terms of global effects, we have already encountered the potential effect of sulphur compounds in forming clouds. Across most industrial nations, tiny particles of sulphuric acid in the air reduce visibility by forming what are popularly but misleadingly known in summer as 'heat hazes'. Today, in most parts of the industrialized world, the problem from sulphuric acid is receding as power stations filter sulphur dioxide from their emissions. Attention is beginning to focus on the nitrogen emissions. Besides causing acidification, they have a wider range of other effects on the atmosphere, including the formation of ozone near to the ground.

Ozone is a confusing gas. It is supposed to be the stuff that makes a visit to the seaside so enervating. Yet the seaside smell is not ozone at all, and any ozone that is around is more likely to give you asthma than a happy holiday. Then there is the confusion between whether ozone is a good or a bad thing. The truth is that it is a Jekyll and Hyde of a gas. Dr Jekyll is the stratosphere, keeping the planet safe for life. Mr Hyde is down below, close to the ground, endangering life.

Ozone near the ground does contribute to the atmosphere's protective shield of ozone, but the effect is small since only 10% of the world's ozone is in the troposphere. More important at these close quarters is the fact that ozone is toxic, especially to plants, at concentrations dangerously close to today's average levels. Ozone is widely regarded as a factor in the strange death of trees in Europe and North America during the 1980s. About a century ago, ozone levels near the ground were around 10 ppb. Today, background levels are at least 20 ppb and concentrations sometimes reach 200 ppb.

One of the world's top experts on tropospheric ozone, Stuart Penkett from the University of East Anglia in England, believes this increase is 'as remarkable as the . . . ozone hole and potentially just as consequential'. The cause of this increase is pollution, especially from cars. Ozone is created by the reactions of a wide range of hydrocarbons and nitrogen oxides in sunlight. Car exhausts contain both these chemicals in large amounts and urban photochemical smogs are potent generators of ozone. On hot summer days, as the motorists of Europe and North America head for the sea or the countryside, they slam the atmosphere's ozone-making machine into top gear. By the afternoon, ozone levels for hundreds of kilometres downwind of big urban areas soar to 100 ppb or more. If the hot weather persists, the pool of ozone intensifies and spreads. Ozone reached record levels in much of the US during the long hot summer of 1988.

In the 1970s, atmospheric scientists in Europe wanted to measure the extent of ozone pollution in summer. They looked for somewhere pollution-free as a benchmark. They chose Adrigole, a small town on the south coast of Ireland. But, to their horror, they discovered that ozone levels were sometimes as high at Adrigole as elsewhere, at more than 100 ppb. Europe's ozone fog had extended out into the Atlantic and engulfed Ireland.

Some plants do not mind ozone at all. French researchers have found that summers with lots of ozone around produce vintage years in the Rhine and Mosel vineyards. Perhaps ozone helps to grow good wine in California, too. But at more than 100 ppb ozone is a real hazard. Many plants undoubtedly suffered in Britain during the long hot European summer of 1976 when ozone levels ranged up to 240 ppb.

It is now clear that the leftovers of intense summer smogs are creating a general year-round accumulation in ozone throughout the lower atmosphere of the northern hemisphere. Man-made hydrocarbons such as ethane, propane, acetylene and benzene accumulate even over the Arctic in winter. They are converted to ozone in the spring. Penkett says: 'The type of photochemistry responsible for the Los Angeles type of smog is occurring throughout large parts of the northern hemisphere troposphere.'

Nature is not completely innocent in all this. There are a lot of naturally produced hydrocarbons in the atmosphere, including methane and isoprenes given off by trees. Hydrocarbons usually provide the scent for plants and one recent estimate put the output of hydrocarbons other than methane from the world's plants at a billion tonnes a year, ten times the output from industry and cars. Isoprenes probably account for a third of this, a fact that provided the grain of truth behind Ronald Reagan's notorious remark in 1980, shortly before his election as American president, that 'approximately 80% of our air pollution stems from hydrocarbons released by vegetation.'

But the second ingredient required for ozone generation in the lower atmosphere is nitrogen oxides, which come mainly from human activities. For practical purposes, nitrogen oxides control the creation of tropospheric ozone over industrialized countries where levels are highest. Penkett says: 'The lower atmosphere can generate almost an order of magnitude more ozone than it does now, the amount being directly proportional to the concentration of nitrogen oxides in clean air.'

In an article in *Nature* in 1988, Penkett continued: 'The expanding world economy will generate more emissions, particularly of nitrogen oxides which are a mark of an "advanced" economy. This will probably cause the source areas to spread and intensify ozone production, at least in the northern hemisphere.' I need hardly add, as a footnote, that tropospheric ozone is yet another greenhouse gas.

11

BEFORE THE FLOOD

GOODBYE KIRIBATI

One of the most devastating consequences of greenhouse warming will be floods. *The Times* of London, not quite the staid organ it once was, leapt at the story in August 1987. The first scientist to assess the flooding risks for Britain had made his findings public at a science conference in Belfast. 'Huge tides threaten to engulf Britain, researchers predict', ran the headline. 'Huge rises in sea levels threaten to devastate much of Britain, causing catastrophic loss of life in the next century, if expert predictions are accurate. Much of London and the Thames estuary would be engulfed by inrushing tides . . . '

The article, based on a lecture by Bill Carter of the Department of Environmental Studies at the University of Ulster, included a map identifying 25 places at risk round the coasts of the British Isles. Oddly, it did not include London, presumably because Carter believes the Thames barrier will be sufficient protection. But it did include the centres of Aberdeen and Dublin, several entire Hebridean islands, the coastlines of Essex, north Kent and Lincolnshire, the Norfolk Broads and two nuclear power stations at Dungeness in Kent.

Most estimates suggest that the world's sea levels could rise by a metre or so within the next century because of the expansion of sea water as it warms and the melting of ice sheets on land. (The loss of ice sheets floating in the Arctic Ocean will have no effect, just as a gin and tonic does not overflow when the ice melts.)

For many countries, the impact could be serious. In 1986 the Dutch completed a barrier across the mouth of the River Scheldt to prevent flooding of the kind that killed 2,000 people in 1953. It was just four kilometres long, but cost more than $3 billion. At $800 million a kilometre, the cost of such protection round the world would run to many trillions of dollars. Bangladesh has millions of people living a metre or so above sea level. In 1970 a tidal surge in the Bay of Bengal killed 300,000 people living in the Ganges delta. A rise in seas of 50 centimetres by, say, 2040 would permanently flood 12% of the country.

Who is going to pay for a barrier to protect Bangladeshis from the Bay of Bengal, or to stop the Mediterranean invading the Nile delta? A one-metre rise in sea level would flood a sixth of Egypt's farmland and make eight million people homeless. London may be able to protect itself. Doubtless, the US government could defend against the prospect of the sea washing up the Potomac River and lapping at the lawns of the White House. Australia could probably keep Botany Bay out of the Sydney Opera House. But the Ganges delta, the coastal plain of China and the many vulnerable tropical islands are a different matter. The Netherlands already spends 6% of its gross national product on protecting its coast from the North Sea. Could Guyana contemplate doing the same? Stjepan Keckes, who is in charge of oceans at the UN Environment Programme, says that within 30 years, the inhabited islands of Kiribati (formerly the Gilbert Islands) could disappear beneath the Pacific Ocean — the first nation to be obliterated by the greenhouse effect. Where will the 60,000 inhabitants of Kiribati go? And who will look after the 180,000 people on the 220 inhabited islands of the Maldives in the Indian Ocean, where virtually no land is more than two metres above the current sea level? Then there is Tuvalu. In October 1988, ten years to the week after the former Ellis Islands won independence from Britain, the UNEP reported that the country's nine coral islands would be 'uninhabitable by the middle of the next century'.

Some researchers point out that a warmer atmosphere will evaporate more water from the sea, which might keep down sea levels. However, most believe that what goes up will come down again as rain. During the past century, in which global temperatures have risen by half a degree or so, sea levels have risen by some ten centimetres. This is mostly due to the expansion of the water in the warmer oceans, though mountain glaciers have been in retreat for a century, especially in the tropics. The Rhône glacier in the Swiss Alps is a famous example. Mount Kenya in East Africa had eighteen glaciers in 1889; today only ten remain. The rise in sea levels would have been perhaps fifteen millimetres greater had not humans stored ever more water in reservoirs on land. The dams on the River Colorado in the western US, for instance, hold back the equivalent of four years of the river's flow.

Tom Wigley, who runs the Climatic Research Unit at the University of East Anglia in England, predicts a rise of perhaps eight centimetres in global sea levels due to thermal expansion of the sea between 1985 and 2025. But much more important is what happens to the great land ice sheets of the world and, in particular, to Antarctic ice.

FAREWELL, THE BAY OF WHALES

On 3 July 1986, two giant icebergs broke off from the Filchner ice shelf, one of the largest of several thick sheets of ice that hang on to the edge of Antarctica and extend out into the surrounding waters. The icebergs cast themselves off into the Weddell Sea, and headed slowly towards the Falkland Islands. The largest of these chunks of ice measured 15,000 square kilometres and took a Russian scientific research station called Druzhnaya with it. It was as if New Jersey or Yorkshire or half of Belgium had suddenly drifted off into the sea. The event coincided with the breakout of another giant iceberg, measuring 6,000 square kilometres, from the Larsen ice shelf on the other side of the Weddell Sea. The total loss of ice from the Antarctic totalled 6,000 cubic kilometres.

A year later, in October 1987, another chunk of ice broke off from the Ross ice shelf, on the other side of the continent. This one was 150 kilometres across and perhaps 250 metres thick. Its cliffs, known to mariners as the Bay of Whales, appear in atlases. But they have gone for ever, melted somewhere in the Southern Ocean on the way to New Zealand. The number of large icebergs breaking loose, or 'calving', from Antarctica increased dramatically in the late 1980s. Indeed, the recent loss of ice may be unprecedented.

All this could be part of the natural rhythm of the ice shelves. The Filchner ice shelf had been moving forward steadily at about a kilometre a year for 30 years without shedding much ice. Parts of the Ross ice shelf have not 'calved' since before Amundsen and Scott trekked across the shelf to the South Pole in 1911. Perhaps this is normal. Shelves advance for a few decades; then lots of ice breaks off the end; then the advance resumes. But we cannot assume this. The sudden outbreak of calving coincides with a decade in which the southern hemisphere has experienced seven of its eight warmest years on record.

The Antarctic continent supports a vast reservoir of frozen water. The continent covers some 13 million square kilometres, 1.5 times the size of the US, and is topped by a layer of ice that averages 2.5 kilometres thick. It holds 91% of all the ice in store on land. Greenland holds 8% and all the mountain glaciers of the world, from Alaska to the Alps, hold the remaining 1%. If all the Antarctic ice melted tomorrow, sea levels round the world would rise by 60 metres — enough to flood most of the world's cities and much of the farmland.

The continent's ice is made up of two main sheets. The larger is the East Antarctic ice sheet. If this melted, sea levels would rise almost 54 metres. Most researchers do not believe this likely. Even if temperatures warmed substantially, the sheet would remain in place, they say. Indeed, it might grow if warming increased snowfall. But a thicker ice sheet might be a less stable one.

The general view until recently was that the East Antarctic ice sheet had been in place for more than ten million years. But now that view is being challenged. Ann Henderson-Sellers, a British geographer now in Australia, points out that:

171

About 95,000 years ago, there was a sudden rise in sea level by between fifteen and twenty metres over a period of less than a century. It is likely that this was due to a 'surge' of the East Antarctic ice sheet, with a large proportion of its mass suddenly sliding into the sea. Such a surge might, perhaps, be the consequence of a build-up of ice of the kind resulting from increased evaporation [and hence snowfall] in a warmer world.

In 1986 American researchers reported finding ancient plants and fossilized wood with roots in two-million-year-old rocks in the Transantarctic mountains close to the South Pole. At around the same time, Australians found the remains of dolphins close by. There were once green hills in Antarctica. Temperatures must have been around 10°C. That is 20° warmer than today. Streams ran near the pole, says Peter Webb from the Institute of Polar Studies at Ohio State University. 'We believe that the [East Antarctic] ice sheet is very unstable,' he said.

The state of the second sheet, covering the West Antarctic, remains of greatest immediate concern, however. This sheet has a complex structure. It is essentially a marine ice sheet tethered to an archipelago of islands, some rising above sea level but others submerged by as much as 2.5 kilometres. Most of the ice sheet is already displacing water, so the effect of its disappearance on sea levels would be much smaller than for the East Antarctic sheet. It would raise sea levels by only about six metres. But there is a distinct possibility that this could happen, perhaps within a few decades.

Henderson-Sellers puts the argument this way:

The West Antarctic ice sheet is particularly vulnerable . . . because most of it is not grounded on the sea floor. Instead, it is supported by many submarine mountains or hills, like pillars holding up a massive ice roof. As a result, temperature changes, a rise in sea level and storm surges could easily combine to lift large regions of the ice free from its support, so that it breaks up and the pieces drift to higher latitudes and temperatures and melt.

172

Before the Flood

Some researchers believe that the destruction of the West Antarctic ice sheet could happen soon. John Mercer of the Institute of Polar Studies at the Ohio State University believes that 'a major disaster — a rapid five-metre rise in sea level, caused by deglaciation of the West Antarctic — may be imminent or in progress after atmospheric carbon dioxide content has only doubled . . . within about 40 years.' Just 125,000 years ago, at the height of the last interglacial era, the West Antarctic ice sheet did disintegrate, raising sea levels by five to six metres. It may have happened swiftly, within 100 years or so, says Mercer.

The sheet is very vulnerable to warmer ocean waters, which can wash beneath the ice, melting it from below. Warm water below, rather than warm air above, will be the main method of melting. In order to survive, says Mercer, the West Antarctic ice needs colder summers, perhaps as much as 10°C colder, than does the East Antarctic ice.

A second source of vulnerability arises because much of the ice sheet is kept in place only because it is trapped. On two sides it is held in place by a string of ice-covered islands. On the other two sides, it is kept fast by two large ice shelves: the combined Ronne-Filchner shelf in the Weddell Sea and the Ross shelf. The shelves act like corks in a bottle, allowing ice to accumulate behind them far below sea level. Mercer says: 'The marine ice sheet in West Antarctica can exist only so long as [it] is buttressed by [these two] shelves.' If the shelves disappear, 'ice cover would be confined to areas above sea level'. Any sign of the shelves retreating, as they are today, is therefore cause for alarm.

There may be a critical temperature for these ice shelves, above which summer melting would destroy more ice than accumulates in winter. Around Antarctica, no ice shelves exist where the average sea temperature in the warmest month (January) is greater than freezing point. The Ross and Ronne-Filchner ice sheets do not extend into water as warm as this because there is not enough snow falling in their catchments to sustain such large shelves. Their limits are in sea with a warmest temperature of around minus 4 to minus 5°C. So, despite the recent signs of calving from both shelves, the theory suggests that they should survive intact a warming of the sea of up to 5°.

173

Climate models suggest that the greenhouse warming will be more intense in polar regions, because when ice begins to melt the land and oceans will absorb more of the Sun's heat. The models predict a warming of 10°C or more within 50 years at the latitude of the ice shelves.

Says Mercer: 'Once this level of comparative warmth had been reached, deglaciation would probably be rapid, perhaps catastrophically so, because even a small additional rise in temperature would affect a large expanse of gently sloping ice.' Terrence Hughes from the University of Maine describes the event more dramatically: 'A relatively minor climatic fluctuation along the ice shelf calving barrier can unleash dynamic processes independent of climate that cause calving bays to remorselessly carve out the living heart of a marine ice sheet.'

Hughes offers as a model for what might happen in Antarctica the fate of the great Laurentian ice sheet that covered Canada at the end of the last ice age. The main ice sheet on land (the equivalent of the East Antarctica sheet today) melted slowly between 14,000 years ago and 8,000 years ago. But its central portion, rather like the current West Antarctic sheet, sat in water, in this case the Hudson Bay. It disintegrated much more swiftly, melting or sliding away in less than 500 years.

Has such a process already begun in Antarctica? Small ice shelves north of the Ronne-Filchner shelf, along the Antarctic peninsula, are closer to dangerously warm waters. Satellite pictures reveal that during the 1970s large sections of the Wordie ice shelf on the east of the peninsula broke away and an ice shelf in the George VI channel receded. In 1983 Hughes argued that 'the irreversible retreat of the West Antarctic ice sheet has already begun in the Pine Island Bay sector and will proceed to completion in about 200 years.' It is an open question whether the disintegration has since spread to Ronne-Filchner and Ross, the shelves that bottle up the main West Antarctic ice sheet.

Two major studies of the possible consequences of global warming, published by the US's National Academy of Sciences in 1983 and the International Council of Scientific Unions in 1986, both suggest that, once under way, the melting of the West Antarctic ice sheet would take 'a minimum of 200 years'. The second report conceded that 'other estimates for collapse of the West Antarctic ice sheet range from under 100 years ... the many estimates are tentative because of lack of knowledge of the dynamics of sliding of fast ice streams.'

The timing will depend on how fast the ice shelves melt as warm water washes around beneath them. As soon as the local ocean currents warm, they will melt icebergs in the sea around Antarctica. This will clear a path for more warm water to infiltrate beneath the ice shelves, which will in turn speed up the melting. Several researchers suggest that once a critical figure of about one metre of melting per year is reached the shelves will be doomed. The shelf in the George VI channel is melting today at two metres per year. Mercer believes that the Ross shelf, which is anchored only very precariously to the sea floor, will be the first to lose its anchors and float away, 'uncorking' the West Antarctic ice sheet. William Budd from the Meteorology Department at the University of Melbourne says that warming of the oceans could soon cause melting 'in excess of ten metres per year, which could largely remove the present large ice shelves in less than a century'.

Whether it happens in 100 years or 700, the prospect is alarming. Sea levels six metres higher than today would inundate Hamburg, New York, Beijing, Seoul, London, Bangkok and Sydney. New Orleans, Venice, Galveston, Cairo and Shanghai would have long gone. Much of Washington DC would be uninhabitable. You could row a boat from Capitol Hill to the White House. Miami would be reduced to a maze of tall buildings poking through the waves several tens of kilometres from the new shoreline of a rather smaller Florida than today. Those fourteen cities alone are home to some 80 million people.

12

A QUESTION OF NUMBERS

LIMITS TO GROWTH?

Scientists who warn of disasters are usually guaranteed a good audience. When they are well-heeled, come from a fashionable institution and have a top-flight PR company to sell their message, the effect can be dramatic. That was how Dennis and Donella Meadows took the world by storm in February 1972 with a slim volume called *The Limits to Growth*. Backed by an Italian millionaire and his private organization, the Club of Rome, and with the help of 12,000 free copies of the book distributed to ministers and journalists round the world, they succeeded in persuading millions of people that their computer model predicting a global apocalypse should be taken seriously.

Put simply, the Meadows and their computer predicted that unless current world trends in population growth and industrial output are checked, and unless pollution is severely curtailed, our civilization faces a catastrophic collapse within 100 years, perhaps within 50.

Computers seemed awesome in the early 1970s, and so did the Massachusetts Institute of Technology, where Dennis Meadows was a systems analyst. As the British magazine, *New Internationalist*, put it at the time: 'Computer portents of doom have a power to impress and terrorize which the ordinary mortal does not possess. The cool reasonability and the inevitability which attends the hundreds of millions of microcircuits, seems to banish all possibility of argument.'

The computer model, run on an IBM 2001, could today be

A Question of Numbers

fitted on to many home computers and its predictions appear
more the stuff of computer games than science. But at the
time they had great power. Roger Revelle, then the chief of
Harvard's Population Research Center, called the study 'a
really important contribution'. *Science*, the premier American
scientific journal, ran an article on the study across five
pages, though it viewed the launch in the Romanesque
Great Hall of the Smithsonian Institution in Washington
primarily as theatre.

The essence of the story is familiar: spiralling economic
and population growth, along with pollution, are outstripping the ability of humankind to grow food and find raw
materials to sustain modern civilization. The trouble was
that this conclusion had been essentially 'fixed' by the way
the computer was programmed. Meadows told the computer
to assume that all the bad things, pollution and our demands
for soils and mineral reserves, increased exponentially, i.e.
at an ever-accelerating rate. All the good things, notably
technological breakthroughs, continued to grow at the
current rate. Not surprisingly, the computer predicted a
bumpy ride for humanity.

Thus, the report said, 'there will be a desperate land
shortage before the year 2000 if per capita land requirements
... remain as they are today.' A big 'if', that. It appears to
assume no technological advances at all. The computer also
predicted that many natural resources, from aluminium to
oil, would run out. This arose because the Meadows arbitrarily
assumed that only five times the present known reserves
would ever be exploitable. They also guessed that if pollution rates (a term that went undefined) rose a hundred
times, then death rates from disease and poisoning would
soar. Galactic invaders in arcade games have obliterated the
Earth on the basis of more sophisticated analysis.

In the 'standard world model', said the report,

as resource prices rise and mines are depleted, more and
more capital must be used for obtaining resources, leaving
less to be invested for future growth. Finally, investment
cannot keep up ... and the industrial base collapses,
taking with it the service and agricultural systems ...

177

Population finally decreases [in around 2050] when the death rate is driven upward by lack of food and health services.

In other runs of the computer model, using slightly different assumptions, rampant pollution or overworked farmland triggered the inevitable catastrophe.

For Aurelio Peccei, the Italian godfather of the project, the report's conclusions were 'preliminary, but it is a key which permits every layman to enter the labyrinth of the fantastic problems towering over mankind'. Critics saw a more sinister purpose. They feared the political impact of Peccei's call for an end to economic growth. It seemed to echo the message of another messianic doom-monger almost 200 years before. Thomas Malthus believed populations always grew in size until they self-destructed. He used this theory to argue against the British Poor Laws and said the rich should not help the poor because it would provide only a temporary respite against an even greater disaster.

At the launch of *The Limits to Growth*, someone from the American Cancer Society asked: 'Is pharmaceutical research to prolong life immoral?' Press reports said that Dennis Meadows 'sidestepped' the question. One critic accused the Meadows of being 'elitists trying to kick down the ladder of growth after climbing up themselves'. One of their senior colleagues at MIT told *Science* that they were 'providing simple-minded answers for simple-minded people who are scared to death. And that's a dangerous thing. The messianic impulse is what disturbs me.'

In 1972 another young scientist was making his name on the apocalypse circuit. He was Paul Ehrlich, an imposing, talkative and highly quotable population biologist from California. He spent much of his time watching butterflies and had noted how, given the right conditions, they would breed so fast that they demolished all the types of plant leaves which they had evolved to eat, and become extinct. Taking a leaf out of Malthus's book, Ehrlich transferred the lesson of the Californian butterflies to humans. His best-selling tome, *The Population Bomb*, offered three possible futures. In the first, a billion people (almost a quarter of the world's population) would starve to death between 1973 and 1983. In the second, rampant disease halted population growth by 1984; and the third postulated that after a crusade by the Pope in favour of birth control, the billionth death from starvation was delayed until 1990. He wrote:

> The battle to feed all of humanity is over ... Nothing could be more misleading to our children than our present affluent society. They will inherit a totally different world, a world in which the standards, politics and economics of the past are dead.

The scientific beginning for this exposition may have been butterflies, but the emotional beginning was even more interesting. It began, he said, in a late-night taxi ride through Delhi. 'The streets seemed alive with people,' he wrote.

> People eating, people washing, people sleeping, people visiting, arguing and screaming. People thrusting their hands through the taxi window begging ... People, people, people, people. As we moved through the mob, hand horn squealing, the dust, noise, heat and cooking fires gave the scene a hellish aspect. Would we ever get to our hotel? All three of us were, frankly, frightened.

John Caldwell, an eminent Australian demographer whose speciality is people rather than butterflies, points out acidly:

> [Ehrlich] did not see population explosion, for Delhi's birth rate is relatively low. He probably saw fewer people than one would see with pleasure in New York, London or Paris at Christmas or in the peak hour. What he did see was poor non-Europeans.

FALSE PROPHECIES

Ehrlich's predictions have not come true. There are few signs that the Meadows' *The Limits to Growth* have any practical meaning. The simple idea of pollution bringing disease and poisoning does not seem likely today. But such ideas still hold great sway. The heart of the matter is the idea that there is some law of diminishing returns — that humans will find it ever more difficult to sustain and extend the way of life developed in the affluent countries. Is it true?

Let us take raw materials, the 'limiting factor' for economic growth identified in the Meadows' standard model. Little more than a year after the publication of *The Limits to Growth* came the decision by the OPEC cartel of oil producers to quadruple their prices almost overnight. It brought terrifying immediacy to fears that the world would run out of the staples of industrial society. Was the resource crisis upon us? As the apparently unending growth of the world's economies since 1945 lurched to a standstill, the answer appeared to be 'yes'. During the 1970s, fears for the future continued, culminating in the deeply pessimistic *Global 2000 Report to the President*, commissioned by Jimmy Carter in 1977 and presented to him in 1980. One consequence was that countries began to build up stocks of 'strategic minerals', such as cobalt and titanium.

People have for many years predicted that one or other critical resource will run out. They predicted the end of oil in the 1880s. But such predictions usually act as a spur either to the discovery of new reserves or to the development of substitutes. The importance that *The Limits to Growth* and others in the panicky 1970s placed on known reserves of key materials was quite misplaced. For oil, perhaps the most strategic material of all, the cost of prospecting is almost half the total cost of extracting the oil. Therefore known reserves are always small, limited by the planning needs of the oil companies.

Despite the rapacious demands of post-war industry, the known reserves of most important minerals continue to rise year by year. In 1972 copper, one of the most widely used minerals, had known reserves sufficient to last only until 2010. A decade later, enough new reserves had been identified to last until 2045. Moreover, technological advance was set to make exploitable many more sources.

A study in 1984 by Alexander Zucker from the Oak Ridge National Laboratory in Tennessee concluded that 'it appears unlikely that the world will run short of any element before about 2050. This provides considerable time to develop new technology to economically exploit lower grade and alternative ones to bring some 30 elements into essentially infinite supply and to use these elements in developing substitutes to satisfy the requirements of modern civilized societies.'

In the past decade, technological developments have given this optimistic scenario substance and left threadbare the pessimism of *The Limits to Growth*. Ceramics made from clay can now replace many minerals in short supply, including tungsten and cobalt. The hardness and resistance to high temperatures and corrosion that ceramics display will make them ideal in cutting tools and for myriad purposes in engines and heat exchangers. Another common material, sand, makes glass which is now being turned into optical fibres. These will replace copper in most telecommunications cables. New composite materials, matrices of carbon or glass fibres held together by resin, will take over from metal alloys, in jet engines for instance.

There was a world cobalt crisis in 1978 after an inopportune war cut supplies. We now know that nodules on the sea bed contain 7,500 years' worth of the stuff. They await our need to exploit them. When low-grade ores can be better exploited, supplies of iron and aluminium will also be 'near infinite' says Zucker.

Part of the Meadows' case was that it would cost so much to recover resources in the twenty-first century that the global economy could not take the strain. After the OPEC oil crisis, many economists assumed that resources in future would be more expensive. President Carter's Global 2000 Report predicted that 'the real price of energy will rise more than 150% between 1975 and 2000.' This, it said, would lift the cost of fertilizers and be a prime reason for a 95% rise in food prices. But by the late 1980s, oil prices were lower than in the early 1970s.

In 1981 Julian Simon from the University of Illinois wrote an heretical book, *The Ultimate Resource*, which pointed out that for at least the past 200 years the real price of fuel, metals, food and every other natural resource has fallen. Simon saw no reason for that trend to change. There was no law of diminishing returns, he said. Zucker looked at the issue another way. He wondered what the capital investment would need to be between now and the year 2100 to fulfil his target of bringing 30 key elements into 'infinite supply'. He came up with a total bill up to the year 2100 of $10 trillion. He concluded that this was 'not unreasonable since it amounts to less than 0.2% of the cumulative world gross national product'.

Simon's 'ultimate resource', which gave the title to his book, is human inventiveness. He believes that improvements in technology will, as they have in the past, keep ahead of the challenges facing our species. When elephant tusks grew scarce, he says, people looked for a substitute for ivory billiard balls and came up with plastics. 'People create additional resources ... raw materials have become less scarce throughout history,' he says. 'The main fuel to speed the world's progress is our stock of human knowledge. Our ultimate resource is skilled, spirited and hopeful people exerting their wills and imaginations to provide for themselves and for their families, and thereby provide for the benefit of us all.'

Here we have reached a central conundrum for all futurologists. Put at its simplest, it is a battle between the optimists and the pessimists. It is a thread that runs through many political, social and economic debates and often transcends conventional political labels. One of its most important manifestations is in debates about the growth in the world's human population. One side sees every new child having less prospect than the last of working its passage aboard spaceship Earth. The other sees unending prospects for more people to do more good for themselves and for the world. For one side, people are mouths to feed; for the other, brains to think and hands to work. For Ehrlich and the Meadows, people are a form of pollution. For Simon they are the ultimate resource.

The more extreme pessimists, such as Malthus 200 years ago and Ehrlich in our own time, see humans on a headlong race to destruction. In 1972 there did seem to be no end to the upward spiral in human population. Yet, in 1973, a few months before the world's economy was thrown out of gear by the oil crisis, the couples of the world started having fewer babies. The rate of growth of the world's population had peaked after two centuries of more or less continuous acceleration and began to subside.

This does not mean population growth has stopped. Far from it. In 1973 the world's population had just hit four billion; in 1987 it passed five billion and the next billion will be with us before the end of the century. But the rate of growth has slowed and, according to predictions by the UN, succeeding billions will start to arrive more slowly after the second decade of the next century. The decline in the number of babies being born is already well under way. In 1973 there were 64 children under fifteen years old for every adult of working age. Today that number is down to 54 and will, according to the UN, reach 38 by 2025. A growing proportion of the increase in numbers will arise because people live longer.

Population historians see nothing unexpected about this. They have identified three periods in human history when population has spurted, before settling down at new higher levels. The first, caused by a revolution in tool-making, occurred a million years ago and took the world's population past a million. The second, beginning some 10,000 years ago at the end of the last ice age, coincided with the development of sedentary agriculture and the rise of the early civilizations. The third is with us today. The world's population has doubled three times since 1700 and seems set to double again by 2100 before settling down once more.

THE POVERTY TRAP

The arguments about why people decide to have fewer children are endless. A common view, shared by the UN's Fund for Population Affairs, is that as communities prosper, parents need fewer children. Offspring are no longer an economic asset, working the fields from a young age or tending their elderly parents. Instead, they need schooling and make it more difficult for both parents to work away from home in offices or factories.

Pessimists say that the poor people of the world will be unable to reach the stage of economic advance where their own immediate economic interest is served by having fewer children. They are stuck in a cycle of poverty which can be broken only by drastic measures to halt population growth. They argue for massive education programmes to persuade the poor to adopt modern methods of birth control. And they agree with Robert MacNamara who in 1973, when President of the World Bank, claimed that 'the greatest single obstacle to the economic and social development of the majority of the people in the underdeveloped world is rampant population growth.'

The optimists say that peasants usually have large families because this is in their own best interests, and that it is usually also in the interests of their communities and countries. Empty countries, such as those on the edge of the Sahara, need many more people in order to develop, certainly not fewer. Large populations would enable local markets in food to develop and would make the construction of roads and railways worthwhile. Peasants would then cease to rely on subsistence farming and the vagaries of the weather, and could begin to join the cash economy.

During the nineteenth century, Europe and North America combined record rates of growth in population with record increases in prosperity. In the past 40 years, many poor nations have surged ahead despite (or perhaps because of) fast-rising populations. Taiwan, Hong Kong, Malaysia, Kenya, the Ivory Coast and Brazil all fall into this category. If there is no law of diminishing returns, then the rest of the world ought to be able to join it too.

Among the 30 poorest countries in the world, those that improved most the average wealth of their inhabitants between the mid-1960s and the mid-1980s were China, Pakistan, Kenya, Sri Lanka and Malawi. Had they been helped by a lower growth in population? Far from it. Population growth in these countries averaged 2.7% per year. The worst economic performers were Chad, Niger, Ghana, Uganda and Madagascar. Their population growths were slightly lower, averaging 2.6% per year.

Edouard Saouma, then director-general of the UN's Food

and Agriculture Organization, claimed in the mid-1980s that 'many African countries, if they do not take action to encourage a drop in fertility rates, are speeding headlong to disaster.' Yet, where is the evidence? Africa's ten richest countries have virtually the same population growth rates as the ten poorest. Kenya had the fastest growth in population in the world throughout the 1970s and 1980s at 3.6% per year. Nonetheless, it sustained an increase in wealth for each of its inhabitants that averaged 2.8% per year.

Figures such as these led the US's National Research Council to conclude in 1986 that there was 'no necessary relation' between population growth and the exhaustion of common resources. The dangers of fast population growth were, it said, largely those of the failure of government institutions to respond and adapt. One member of the council's committee, Samuel Preston, who was also director of the Population Studies Center at the University of Pennsylvania, said: 'Rapid population growth in most places is a relatively minor factor.' Despite the fears of the 1970s, 'we haven't gone to hell in a handbasket.'

Even in one of the most fragile environments of all, on the edge of the Sahara, there is strong evidence that more people can be a good thing. The area around the northern Nigerian city of Kano has a population density of 650 people per square kilometre, one of the highest in Africa. Yet it is probably the richest part of the Sahel. Why? Because people have been able to become less dependent on the land. John Caldwell, an Australian demographer, points out that the conventional wisdom among colonial administrators in French West Africa was that economic development would only be possible in the region when there were more people, not fewer.

FLIGHT TO THE CITIES

Today migration, especially to the cities, is a key element of change in the development of the Third World. Most peasants with an itch to improve their lot do not wait for change, they head for greener pastures, or, most frequently, the cities. Burkina Faso (formerly Upper Volta), on the fringes of the Sahara, 'faces abject poverty for decades to come', according to the World Bank. Its inhabitants agree. More than a million of them, a sixth of the population, have left since the early 1970s, mostly for the neighbouring Ivory Coast and its capital Abidjan, where life is better. A further half million people have left neighbouring Mali, also for the Ivory Coast.

Between 1973 and 1983 the UN estimates that the world's urban population increased by 30%. This is widely regarded as a bad thing. Stories of shanty towns, beggars on the street and tribes of orphan children suggest a grim fate for the unwary peasant who seeks, if not streets paved with gold, at least streets that are paved. Yet the peasants continue to vote for the cities with their feet. Abidjan keeps booming and a UN expert group reported at the height of the influx from the Sahel that 'the city benefits from the labour force of migrants . . . Migrants and their families are generally better off . . . the relatively low rate of unemployment among migrants comes as a surprise.' For many, the attempt to step from the Third World to the First has been successful.

Remember Calcutta, a symbol of the Third World's hopeless millions in the 1960s? A recent investigation by the International Planned Parenthood Federation, no friend of population growth, concluded that 'over the years, migration has brought the city prosperity.'

Do the villagers back home suffer? Usually not. According to the World Bank, farm productivity is maintained in Mali and in Burkina Faso, and rural incomes have risen as the money sent home by migrants has become an important source of investment.

Caldwell, in an important study of the drought years in the Sahel, concluded in 1984 that migration to the cities is 'probably the major way of relieving population pressures in arid rural areas and also the major way of providing markets for agricultural produce so as to raise rural living standards'. Kano may turn out to be the future for the Sahel. The rapid expansion of cities in the Third World is not something that should frighten us.

The case for optimism in these arguments is, in my view, very strong. In the early part of this book we looked at the potential for developing sustainable agriculture in Africa, where the popular image is of a hopelessly degraded environment, and in the Amazon basin. We might also have looked at how new technologies are allowing the deserts and salty soils to bloom. The claim that we will run out of resources for industry now seems feeble and, even assuming more people to be a bad thing, it seems the population bomb has been defused. Barring global catastrophe, there are no limits to growth other than those of political ineptitude. The issue of greatest concern is whether, by upsetting the oceans or atmosphere, we might unwittingly bring on such a global catastrophe. And that is the central theme of this book.

13

TURNING DOWN THE HEAT

Technical fixes are beguiling. They offer simple solutions to complex problems. Some sound crazy. Acid rain is killlng the fish in Norwegian lakes? Britain's Central Electricity Generating Board suggests that the Norwegians should charter a fleet of helicopters to bombard their lakes with lime to neutralize the acid. Others are accepted practice. The deserts are advancing? The UN spends millions of dollars planting trees to hold back the sands.

The brouhaha over the ozone hole did not take long to throw up the first scheme to plug it. On 9 November 1987 an American magazine, *Chemical and Engineering News*, published a letter from Leon Sadler of the University of Alabama. If we are destroying ozone in the stratosphere, he said, then why not make some more and take it up there as a replacement. 'If there really is an ozone problem, then we have the means to do something about it,' he said. 'Such a project might represent one of those rare instances in which mankind is able to undo some of the damage that it has done to the environment.'

Sadler had done his sums. He started with the proposition that we might continue to emit CFCs into the atmosphere at roughly the current rate and that this might reduce the ozone layer by some 6% over the next century. To meet that decline, he proposed a long-term programme of ozone injection into the stratosphere. Put like that, it sounds plausible.

The ozone layer is quite thin. At ground-level pressures, it is only about three millimetres thick. The entire layer contains three billion tonnes of pure ozone. 'If the projected 6% depletion is to be replaced over 100 years, the average rate of replenishment required would be only 5.4 million kilograms per day.' That is roughly the output of three large modern chemical plants producing gases.

Sadler suggests several methods of propelling the ozone into the stratosphere. You could hitch small generators to ordinary commercial and military aircraft, which could spray ozone as they go about their usual flights; you could use 'guns' to shoot frozen ozone 'bullets' into the upper atmosphere; you could send up balloons equipped with solar-powered ozone generators; or you could fly special aircraft from a number of world ozone production centres. The cargo capacity required for this last method, said Sadler, would represent only 2% of the US airlines' current freight load.

The idea sank without trace. No international body declared its support. No entrepreneur offered to do the job. And yet it is not daft. CFCs take so long to reach the ozone layer that it will be many decades before the Montreal Protocol limiting their future production has any effect. Ozone injection would work much more quickly. It might not prevent the ozone holes forming over the poles, but it could probably stop those holes draining the ozone shield round the rest of the planet. Sadler's strategy may one day be seen as a sensible project to preserve a 'global common'.

Our planet is in need of a new stewardship, based on a scientific understanding of how it works. But we are a very long way from achieving that end. We have only the vaguest idea of what controls there are in the cockpit of spaceship Earth. While we are drawing up the operating manual, we may have to come up with some short-term technical fixes to help us to get by.

We may, for instance, have to turn to an idea expounded at length in 1986 by Walter Newman and Rhodes Fairbridge of City University and Columbia University, both in New York. As the greenhouse warming raises sea levels, we could attempt to keep down sea levels by storing more water on land. The big dams and aqueducts needed to implement such a plan could be cheaper than flood barriers. The current rise in sea levels of a little over one millimetre a year equals an annual increase in the volume of the oceans of 500 cubic kilometres. If we could keep that much water from reaching the oceans each year we might, they said, halt the rising tides for a while.

We are already unwittingly involved in this 'Canute strategy'. Reservoirs on land regulate around 15% of the annual discharge of the world's rivers. In the past two decades, a third of the expected rise in sea levels from global warming has been counteracted by storage of water in reservoirs and irrigation schemes. In this way we have held back the rising tides for the equivalent of ten to fifteen years over the past century. But other human activities have worked in the opposite direction. We have been liberating massive amounts of 'fossil' water stored in porous rocks under the ground. Projects range from single boreholes sunk into rocks to feed a few cattle, to massive schemes such as Libya's Great Man-made River project. In the US, the vast Ogallala aquifer beneath the Great Plains is in danger of drying up entirely in places. Soviet hydrologists, whose vast irrigation projects require them to make a lot of measurements in cubic kilometres, estimate that the total release of stored water from beneath the ground may raise sea levels by 0.8 millimetres a year. But that takes no account of the water put into farm irrigation systems which leaks away through unlined canals back into the rocks beneath. Whatever the truth, it may now be time to start refilling those underground aquifers.

Newman and Fairbridge proposed that large natural depressions on the surface of the Earth, such as those containing the Caspian and Aral seas in the Soviet Union, could be filled to the brim with water. Their list of the world's great inland drainage basins includes the Imperial Valley in California, a desert that is expensively irrigated from the River Colorado to provide salad vegetables for much of the US. Then there is the Qattara Depression in the desert of north-west Egypt, the Dead Sea valley between Israel and Jordan, and the Eritrea depression around Lake Assale in

Ethiopia. In several cases, engineers already have grandiose plans to divert water into the depressions to generate hydroelectric power. The two researchers say: 'We estimate the storage potential of each of these depressions to be of the order of 1,000 cubic kilometres or more.' One such scheme every two years might hold back the rising sea levels.

The site with the greatest potential, they say, is the Aral-Caspian depression. The surface of the Caspian Sea is already at 28 metres below sea level. 'Raising the level of the Caspian Sea by only ten metres would store 4,420 cubic kilometres of water.' That is eight years of change in sea levels at the current rate of rise. Both the Caspian and Aral seas are dwindling as Soviet engineers divert river water to irrigate the fields of central Asia. The Aral Sea could dry up altogether early next century. The Soviet Union has several times considered a massive transfer of water by canal from Siberian rivers such as the Ob, Yenisey and Lena. If this project went ahead it could, say the two Americans, become a central feature of any international programme to hold back the rise in the world's sea levels.

As we have seen, Lake Chad, in the heart of the African Sahel, once contained many times more water than today. It does not rain much locally, but the lake might be returned to its former size if rain falling on the uplands of the Central African Republic were diverted from the upper valleys of the River Congo into the catchment of the River Chari. This project could also provide water for fields in the Sahel and the extra water in the lake might stimulate evaporation and cloud formation thus reversing the recent desiccation of the region.

For water engineers, these projects are the stuff of dreams. Engineers in the US have for several decades had a plan to divert the water from the Yukon and the River Mackenzie in north-east Canada so that it flows into a giant new reservoir in the Rocky Mountains in the US. The idea was to feed water into the River Colorado. Yukon's water could in this way end up irrigating crops 3,000 kilometres to the south in Arizona and California. When full, the proposed Rocky Mountain Trench reservoir could hold 1,000 cubic kilometres of water, enough to prevent two years' rise in sea levels.

Nobody knows whether such schemes make economic sense, nor what ecological havoc they might cause. If, as expected, the sea levels begin to rise much faster than in the past few decades, then there is probably no choice but to abandon low-lying coastal land. But Newman and Fairbridge are convinced we could slow rises in sea levels for several decades by flooding depressions and refilling inland seas. They suggest that all nations with coasts should contribute to a central fund to support such projects. 'To prevent worldwide [coastal] disaster, new projects must be planned immediately, and be well under way by the end of this century.'

DECARBONIZATION: A COSTLY FIX

Since the 1950s, filters have removed most of the smoke and dust from power station emissions. As a result, cities are much less grimy than in the days when London was known simply as 'the smoke'. During the 1980s many countries installed 'desulphurization' plant at power stations to remove sulphur dioxide, a gas which causes acid rain. This was expensive, but life began to return to lakes and streams from Ontario to Scotland and Scandinavia. Carbon dioxide makes up about 13% of the gas in the chimney of a typical coal-fired power station. Should the next step be to install 'decarbonization' plant? American researchers say that if the equipment were installed at every coal- or oil-fired power station in the US, the annual global release of carbon dioxide from fuel burning would fall by 500 million tonnes, or 10% of the global total. If the whole world did it, the reduction would be at least 30%.

Meyer Steinberg works in the Process Science Division of one of the US government's national laboratories, at Brookhaven. He developed a process to bubble gases from power stations through solvents to remove the carbon dioxide. His process, he admits, would have consumed half of the energy from the power station. A newer system, developed by Dow Chemicals, uses a heat exchanger to extract latent heat from steam produced in the process. That cuts the energy used to 10% of the output of the power station. Perhaps there will be more improvements. Even so, a basic problem remains: how do you lock away permanently all the carbon dioxide?

Steinberg proposes burying it either deep in the ocean or on land in empty gas and oil wells and caverns excavated in salt rocks. An elaborate network of pipes across the US and Europe would carry liquefied carbon dioxide from power stations to the dumping grounds. For most of the world, the cheapest disposal ground would be the oceans.

Shallow seas would not be good enough. Liquid carbon dioxide is less dense than sea water at normal pressures. It would bubble back into the atmosphere. But, says Steinberg, under intense pressure carbon dioxide compresses much more easily than water. Beyond the edges of continental shelves, in the deep ocean below about three kilometres, carbon dioxide becomes denser than sea water. It would 'form a pool of liquid carbon dioxide and sink to the ocean floor'. Europe could dump its carbon dioxide waste on the sea floor at the Straits of Gibraltar, where a deep current running from the Mediterranean to the deep Atlantic would sweep it away. But along the north-east coast of the US, pipelines would have to be 300 kilometres long, threading their way along the continental shelf until they reach the deep ocean.

Steinberg estimates that the massive infrastructure necessary to extract and dump the carbon dioxide into the oceans would roughly double the cost of building a power plant. Electricity prices would rise by 50 to 70%. This sounds like the economics of the madhouse. On the other hand, if laws required electricity producers to dispose of their carbon dioxide in this way, it would certainly encourage them to develop new sources of energy.

A more basic issue is whether the ocean deeps really would hold liquid carbon dioxide in vast pools without eventually bringing them to the surface. Since the water of the deep ocean circulates roughly once every thousand years, our successors might receive a rather unpleasant surprise in about 40 generations' time.

Turning Up the Heat

Maybe the answer is not to plug the source of carbon dioxide but to encourage nature to recycle it. One idea canvassed in 1988 by my colleague John Gribbin is to sprinkle the oceans with iron compounds. If the idea that a shortage of iron often limits biological activity in the ocean turns out to be correct, then this 'iron ration' for the oceans could speed up the biological pump and draw carbon dioxide out of the atmosphere, counteracting the greenhouse effect.

Another promising idea, worked out in some detail by Gregg Marland at the Oak Ridge National Laboratory in the US, is to plant trees. The amount of carbon dioxide put into the atmosphere in the past century by the destruction of forests may aproach 200 billion tonnes, roughly the same as that from burning fossil fuels. Forests and their soils are still the home for some two million million tonnes of carbon. By planting trees to replace those lost, we could quickly moderate the amount of carbon dioxide in the atmosphere.

Marland began thinking about the problem in 1976. He believes that 'although it is impractical to think in terms of solving the carbon dioxide problem through forestry alone, forestry could play a significant role.' He suggests that total emissions of carbon dioxide from burning fossil fuels might double to ten billion tonnes a year 'before a perception of acute ecological disaster and a consensus for action could be achieved'. Perhaps the world would respond if millions died in catastrophic floods in Bangladesh, or the American grain crop was destroyed for two years running, or the forests of northern Europe, Siberia and Canada began to die. Then, if the oceans continued to absorb roughly half the excess carbon dioxide, the task would be to plant trees to take up the other half, that is five billion tonnes a year, 'for a period long enough to allow society to overcome its addiction to fossil fuels'. That would mean establishing new plantations for several decades. After that, as the global plantations reached maturity, we would cut down the wood and store it permanently or use it in a way that prevented its carbon from returning to the atmosphere. Marland suggests a revival of wood as a construction material.

A hectare of sycamore trees in the south-east of the US takes up 7.5 tonnes of carbon per year. At that rate, seven million square kilometres of land should be planted, which is a lot of trees, covering almost the total land area of the US, less Alaska. But it would only add about 20% to the current area of land under forests.

One problem in such a programme would be to decide when to cut down the forests. Mature trees will continue to take up carbon for between 300 and 1,000 years, but only slowly. To keep them sucking carbon out of the air at a maximum rate, trees should be harvested and replaced every few decades. But nobody is clear what that would do to forest soils, which contain as much carbon as the trees themselves. Constant harvesting of trees might cut the carbon capacity of soils too much to make tree planting worthwhile.

Genetic engineering and plant breeding could produce fast-growing trees that suck up lots of carbon. Scientists have already tripled the productivity of certain pine trees in this way. Marland points out that the rates of photosynthesis in trees are typically about half those in modern farm crops. So there is plenty of scope for improvement.

If this sounds too much like a technical 'fix', we can consider instead a grand cycling of carbon as fuel. Why not use some of the wood from the new global plantations as fuel? If we could replace fossil fuels with wood from permanent plantations, the greenhouse effect would be neutralized. The carbon would be cycled endlessly from smokestacks into the atmosphere, back into new forests and thence to power stations again. We would have a renewable source of energy and a tightly managed carbon cycle.

Marland has worked out how much land some large countries would have to plant, in addition to their existing forests, in order to 'take care of their own carbon dioxide in their own closed forests'. West Germany would have the worst problem meeting its target. It would have to plant with trees an area three times its own size. Japan would need to plant 1.3 times its total land area, and the US some 80%. These nations might have to agree to plant trees in other countries, but others could meet their targets within their own borders. And, of course, new fast-growing trees might cut the amount of the land needed for planting.

Marland envisages a world in which twice as much land as today is covered with forests that cycle six times as much carbon as is currently harvested each year. It is, he says, 'physically possible to remove five billion tonnes of carbon per year from the atmosphere either in new forests, in intensively managed forests on existing forest land, or in some combination'. One American power company made a start in 1988 by promising to pay part of the cost of planting 52 million trees in Guatemala — enough to absorb the carbon dioxide to be emitted by a new power station in the US.

TOWARDS A CARBON-EFFICIENT WORLD

Meyer Steinberg, having satisfied himself that 'decarbonization' of gases from power stations is not economically sane, has come up with four other ways to reduce emissions of carbon dioxide. One is to burn natural gas, which emits only about half as much carbon dioxide as coal or oil. Steinberg dismisses this option because there is not enough gas beneath the ground. Many would disagree with that. More worrying is the fact that natural gas is largely made up of methane, which is itself a greenhouse gas, second in importance only to carbon dioxide. Leaks from natural gas pipelines are an important source of methane in the atmosphere, so a switch to burning methane might be jumping from the frying pan into the fire.

Neither nuclear nor solar power create carbon dioxide. A mixture of public opposition, the danger of serious accidents and problems with waste disposal make nuclear energy a tricky option, unless hopes for a new generation of small, safe reactors bear fruit. Nuclear fusion has many hurdles to clear. It is probably a century away from full development. Solar energy, says Steinberg, 'is limited by its low intensity,' though many would guess that solar and hydroelectric power offer the best hopes for electricity generation in the Third World in the next 50 years. During 1988, the beleaguered nuclear power industry argued forcefully that nuclear energy offered a solution to the greenhouse problem. But its opponents argued that energy saving was the most cost-effective response. Bill Keepin and Gregory Kats wrote in *Science* that every dollar invested in energy efficiency would save seven times as much fossil fuel burning as every dollar invested in nuclear power plants. Steinberg believes a global 'Save It' strategy 'could reduce emissions by as much as 60% in the year 2050'.

By 2050, says Steinberg, all offices and homes will have heating systems that recover waste heat, thus cutting fuel bills by 30%. Heat exchangers made of new materials such as ceramics will reclaim the heat from exhaust gases produced inside iron and steel works as well as oil and chemical refineries. They will halve bills in factories. Currently, a typical automobile loses 30% of its energy to friction inside the engine and in axles and transmission. Better engines and lighter bodies could cut the fuel consumption of cars by 65% by 2050. Technologies now on the drawing board, such as fluidized beds, will raise the efficiency with which power stations burn fossil fuels from today's 38% to at least 50%.

A simple extrapolation of current trends in energy use would put emissions of carbon dioxide at seventeen billion tonnes by the year 2050. Steinberg's blueprint would cut that to seven billion tonnes, which is still rather higher than today's five billion tonnes, but it is a start. Steinberg puts the capital cost of his plan for the whole world at $24 million million. But cuts in fuel bills would bring a return on that investment of up to 40%. Moreover, half of his proposed energy savings could be accomplished with 6% of the capital cost — a mere $1.5 million million.

Some researchers look beyond Steinberg's energy-efficient world to a carbon-efficient world, a world which will use coal in ways that do not create carbon dioxide. The International Institute for Applied Systems Analysis, a UN-backed think tank with an impressive pedigree for rigorous thought about practical problems, has developed what it calls a novel integrated energy system for the planet. 'The basic idea,' it says, 'is to decompose and purify the [fossil fuel] before combustion,' and to generate in the process products that are useful, rather than pollutants.

The IIASA draws complicated flow charts showing how

all this could be done. It envisages vast integrated energy works consuming air, water, coal and natural gas and churning out lots of energy, but no pollution. The key ingredients are coal and nuclear power. Electricity would come from nuclear power. Coal would be a feedstock for a chemical works rather than a fuel for burning.

Other people have other versions of an integrated energy world. Leon Green from Energy Conversion Alternatives in the US says that carbon dioxide and methane 'would serve as nutrients for intensive cultivation of biomass'. Gigantic energy centres, especially ones tied to nuclear power, fill most environmentalists with horror. They would much prefer to see solar power, and the harnessing of tidal energy and other renewable resources operated on a small scale under local control. But all agree that, given the political commitment, there are ways of taming the fossil-fuel burners and halting the onward march of the greenhouse effect within a few decades.

THINKING THE UNTHINKABLE

Few people have attempted to marry the assessments of the consequences of global warming and the policies that might meet the threat. But in 1987 Irving Mintzer from the World Resources Institute in Washington published a 'model of warming' which linked predictions of the greenhouse warming with conventional guesses about future world economic growth. His 'high emissions scenario' assumed a growing world addiction to cheap coal in a political climate in which 'national policy makers ignore the environmental risks of energy use, including the greenhouse effect'. His middle way assumed that we continue as now, with rising contributions from nuclear and hydroelectric power and modest improvements in the efficient use of energy. His 'slow build-up scenario' assumed 'strong global efforts' to stabilize the composition of the atmosphere, including a more efficient use of energy, a massive programme of planting trees, and government support for solar energy. In this case, consumption of natural gas soars while burning of coal falls by 75% before 2025.

The results are startling. The middle scenario yields what most researchers expect — a doubling of carbon dioxide from pre-industrial levels by about 2030. But the 'high emissions scenario' brings this date forward to 2015, while the slow build-up postpones it to 2075. Conventional models predict that a doubling in carbon dioxide will bring a warming of between 1.5 and 4.5°C, with the likelihood that it will be at the top end of the range. If the middle scenario is extended to the year 2075, it brings the prospect of a warming of between 2.9 and 8.6°C. The high emissions scenario offers the prospect, within a century, of a warming across the globe of between 5.3° and a staggering 16°C.

Climatologists are currently locked in debate about the impact of an increase of about 4°. This is the maximum likely increase within a century if the world adopted the policies necessary to fulfil the optimistic scenario for a slow build-up of carbon dioxide. They have not seriously begun to address the consequences of increases of 10° or more. Yet millions of people being born today could live to see that happen.

All this, remember, is based on global averages. The models predict that the effects of a doubling of carbon dioxide will be three times greater near the poles. Should we really have to contemplate temperatures rising by up to 50°C over Alaska, northern Siberia and Antarctica in the coming century? It seems extremely unlikely that such a warming could come about. Any self-respecting climate model would blow a fuse by then. But it is the kind of horrific prospect which has led some investigators to predict the wholesale destruction of the Antarctic ice caps, with sea levels rising twenty metres or more, and the infestation of the oceans by vast fleets of giant icebergs. If that happened, they say, the planet's reflectivity would increase so much that the Earth would plunge out of a warming phase into another ice age. That may be a wild idea, but in this kind of territory the current generation of models is just too cosy.

The pace of change is clearly crucial. Human adaptation to the greenhouse effect, whether to counter it or to live with it, is made much harder by the speed of change. One of the themes of this book has been that change tends to be sudden, rather than gradual, and that global averages will hide much bigger changes both in local averages and the frequency of extreme events such as floods and droughts. Nature too responds in different ways to different paces of change. If the climate of a forest changes over thousands or even hundreds of years, the types of trees that grow there will change, too, but gradually and without threatening the survival of the forest. However, the current prediction of a warming of 0.5° per decade is faster than plants can migrate. Such a rapid change will destroy existing trees without providing the time for new species to arrive, propagate and take charge of the forest. The result may be not a new forest but an arid wasteland. And, as George Woodwell made clear, in a global greenhouse the destruction of trees could in the short term intensify warming. The dangers of some runaway greenhouse effect become greater.

The case of the ozone hole has brought home to many scientists how wrong their carefully constituted models can be. Researchers such as Woodwell and Wally Broecker have offered their own ideas of why the models could be wrong. The unexpected is always possible, even probable. The likelihood of extreme events is usually much greater than the computer models would have us believe. The Milankovitch wobbles create only tiny changes in the amount of radiation reaching our planet from the Sun. Yet the wobbles appear able to flip our atmosphere into and out of ice ages. We are only a decade or so away from sending our planet into a 'super-interglacial' era. It will be hotter than at any time for hundreds of thousands of years. This rapid speed of change has probably not been experienced by the planet this side of the last meteorite impact.

John Laurmann from the US Gas Research Institute took up the issue in a guest editorial in the influential journal *Climate Change*, edited by Stephen Schneider. 'The present emphasis on research devoted to the study of scenarios based on the best estimate results in stress being placed on items of low criticality.' He calls this reliance on best estimates a 'dangerous fallacy'. 'The very large uncertainty that seems endemic in the carbon dioxide problem means that the probability of significantly larger and significantly earlier impacts than predicted by the best estimate is by no means negligible, and it is precisely those events that could result in major disruptions to economic and social systems whose studies we should prioritize.' In other words, nobody is looking for the really dangerous things that could happen. He might have added that these greenhouse surprises will also disrupt natural systems the most. Gaia, should she exist, could be overwhelmed.

Laurmann said scientists should throw away their best estimates and turn to 'the modelling of large and rapidly changing climatic perturbations'. They should look for runaway feedbacks which might follow the sudden disintegration of the West Antarctic ice sheet, or the collapse of the northern forests, or the loss of the Gulf Stream.

In 1986 the National Research Council in the US held a workshop on atmospheric change. It was attended by a select group of top climatologists and investigators of global change. Names included Michael McElroy from Harvard, Stephen Schneider from the National Center for Atmospheric Research and Sherry Rowland, the ozone researcher from the University of California at Irvine. They concluded:

We are reluctant to accept a reassuring forecast for a warmer globe ... We know that major changes are likely to produce major unforeseen consequences — indeed the unforecasted Antarctic ozone hole may be just such an example. One might speculate about a host of other possible unforeseen consequences such as the following: In a high carbon dioxide world, would we be overrun by carbon dioxide fertilized weeds? Or would pests become more virulent? Would some traumatic climatic response be triggered as temperatures rise above historical experience, maybe a response triggered by melting ice and snow? Would deserts insidiously spread to envelop major populated areas or croplands? Would the West Antarctic ice pack calve, raising sea levels by up to twenty feet? Would the higher temperatures lead to melting of the Arctic ice pack in summer and produce major unpredictable changes in the weather patterns of the northern hemisphere? Would small shifts in the course of ocean currents produce major changes in regional climates? ...

201

The list could be extended indefinitely, yet we still suspect that many unforeseen consequences will remain uncovered even by these speculative forays.

This is not necessarily a counsel of despair. McElroy chose a conference on 'The Maintenance of the Biosphere' in Edinburgh at the end of 1987 to offer a stirring manifesto on behalf of the future of our planet. It is worth quoting at length.

We live at a unique time in the history of life on Earth. For the first time one species, man, has developed the capacity to change the environment for life on a global scale and to do so within the life of a single member of his species. Change is evident from pole to pole, from the heights of the stratosphere to the depths of the sea ... We have learned to harness reserves of energy gleaned from the Sun over hundreds of millions of years ... Large areas of the land surface have been converted from forest and grassland to agriculture. Fully 10% of the solid surface is now subject to active management. We now have the ability, indeed the obligation, to assess the consequences of our actions ...

We cannot afford to set the clock back. The quality of life is undoubtedly better now than it was 100 years ago. We must learn to apply our growing knowledge of the Earth to chart a wise course to the future ... We need a global strategy to study the Earth ... To accept less than complete understanding is to court disaster. The climate may alter. The location of deserts may shift. Areas once productive may become barren and vice versa. The nature of the air we breathe may change. The flux of ultraviolet radiation may alter. Even the great cycles which mobilize the nutrients essential for life may be affected. We must adopt a different view of the Earth. We must learn to consider it a delicate resource, to be managed and protected. We must learn that it may not be assaulted indefinitely with impunity. The planet as a whole must be treated with the care we now apply only to smaller scales, to national parks, for example. We must not delay. There can be no greater imperative than the need to understand the Earth.

POSTSCRIPT:
ALL ABOARD THE
GAIAN ARK

GENE WRANGLES

Genes are the basic currency of the extraordinary diversity of life on our planet. That is why the new technology of genetic engineering is viewed with such wonder and trepidation. That is why American biologists are planning to spend some $200 million 'mapping' the genes in humans. It is also why many biologists view the destruction of genetic diversity as the most fundamental damage that humans can inflict on the planet. Gaians add that by destroying genetic diversity we are uprooting the Gaian system of regulating the planet. If Gaia has less genetic raw material to work with, her chances of coming up with a way to counter our worst efforts to destroy the planet are decreased.

Peter Raven, the director of the Missouri Botanical Gardens, surveyed the scene of destruction when he gave a keynote address to the 1987 annual meeting of the American Association for the Advancement of Science. He called his lecture: 'The Global Ecosystem in Crisis: We're Killing Our World'. Our world is one 'in which we consume well over a third of total terrestrial photosynthetic productivity, in which human activity threatens to eliminate nearly a quarter of those organisms we do not consume . . .'

The crisis is worst, he said, in the tropical rainforests, the heartlands of biological diversity. They cover just 7% of the world's land surface, yet contain an estimated 2.5 million species, or half of all the land species on the planet. As Raven put it: 'Just under half of the total number of plant species in the world occur only in forests that are rapidly being destroyed.'

An elite group of American biologists, headed by Edmund Wilson, has formed to campaign for the protection of species. Called the 'Club of Earth', it warned in 1986 that: 'The species extinction crisis is a threat to civilization second only to the threat of thermonuclear war. While a majority of the species threatened with extinction are still completely unknown, the result of their loss could be an unprecedented human tragedy.'

Biologists are above all collectors, namers and describers. They catalogue the natural world. So far, they have described about 1.7 million species, including 750,000 insects, 47,000 vertebrates and 250,000 plants. 'The absolute number is likely to exceed five million,' Wilson says. But nobody has much idea of the true total. When Terry Irwin of the US Smithsonian Institution sprayed insecticides into the canopies of trees in rainforests in the Peruvian Amazon basin, he brought down so many different species of beetle that he later estimated there might be some 30 million species of insects alone abroad in the world.

For Alwyn Gentry, a colleague of Raven at the Missouri Botanic Gardens, the Amazon forests of Peru and western Brazil have 'the world's greatest local concentration of species'. He staked out a one-hectare patch of the Yanomano forest in Peru and found 283 species of trees. 'There were only twice as many individuals as species,' he told *Science*.

If we have no idea how many species there are, we have even less idea how many we have destroyed or are likely to destroy. One of the pessimists is Thomas Lovejoy of the World Wide Fund for Nature (formerly the World Wildlife Fund). Lovejoy claims that 'of the three to ten million species now present on the Earth, at least 500,000 will be extinguished during the next two decades.' This, of course, is a wild guess.

Does any of this matter? Is not a bird (or bee or barley seed) in the hand worth several million in the bush? Humans seem to have tried and discarded many more food crops, for instance, than are eaten today anywhere in the world. American Indians once ate more than 1,000 different plant species. Cultivation has changed and narrowed our requirements. Some 95% of the world's food comes from just 30 kinds of plants and three-quarters comes from eight crops. Three species — rice, wheat and corn — supply half our needs.

There are two reasons for maintaining as much of the natural genetic archive as possible. The first is that we never know what species we may need. As Raven put it: 'Oral contraceptives for many years were produced from Mexican yams; muscle relaxants used in surgery come from an Amazonian vine traditionally used to poison darts; the cure for Hodgkin's disease comes from the rosy periwinkle, a native of Madagascar ... ' Who knows what we could find a use for next? The second is that the maintenance of single species can require the constant input of new genes from wild varieties of that species. The genetic sameness of modern high-yielding seed varieties leaves them vulnerable to diseases which can rip across the world. And the precise requirements can change unexpectedly. Plant breeders are now looking for genes which allow crops to survive on saline irrigated fields. Soon, the search will be on for drought-resistant strains of crops for farmers caught out by the greenhouse warming. We may yet need plants, bred for their tolerance to ultraviolet light flooding through a thinning ozone layer. Genetic engineers will have their own requirements. They will increase rather than reduce the need for a diverse gene 'pool' on which to draw.

Where will these genes come from? The answer lies largely in the tropics: in the Amazon basin, the Andes, Mexico, Turkey, Malaysia, Indonesia and a few other countries where, having avoided the biological destruction of the ice ages, genetic diversity has flourished. These areas are known as Vavilov centres, after the Russian botanist who first mapped them.

The stories of genes worth billions of dollars plucked from the edge of extinction in Vavilov centres are legion. Pat Mooney spent seven years researching plant genetic resources for the International Coalition for Development Action. He tells of one Rafael Guzman who, late in 1978, brought a Christmas card up into the Sierra de Manantlan mountain range of western Mexico. The card carried a drawing of *Zea Perennis*, a perennial wild relative of maize that had last been seen in the 1920s. When Guzman came back out of the mountains he had not only redis-covered *Zea Perennis*, he had also found another, vastly more useful perennial, *Zea Diploperennis*, which is resistant to four of maize's seven most prevalent diseases. *Zea Diploperennis* was not discovered wild in the woods. Only one or two thousand plants are known to exist, all on less than two hectares of fenced ground, preserved and pro-tected by an Indian farm family for generations ... Introduce ten Holstein [a breed of cattle] and this billion-dollar resource is gone — for ever.

The world's future wheat and barley farming is threatened, says Mooney, because new barley varieties have replaced traditional ones over half of the heartlands for different strains of barley and wheat in Saudi Arabia and the Lebanon. 'More than 70% of the wheat genetic diversity in these same countries has been replaced by a handful of new varieties such as Mexipack and Sonalika sown over hundreds of thousands of hectares.' Unless the gene pool is preserved, the green revolution could, in this way, self-destruct on its own rapacious success. The Cornwall Brussels sprout is gone for ever and with it the genes of resistance to at least one major crop disease.

The case for preserving genetic diversity is obviously very strong. The world's seeds business has undergone a revo-lution in the 1980s with giant companies such as Shell and Ciba-Geigy cornering the international market. The com-panies are collecting and often patenting varieties and storing them away in vast gene banks. Perhaps this is the only way the job can be done. If genetic resources become property, they would have a value and might stand a better chance of being preserved. If they are commonly owned, they lack value to any individual or company and may be destroyed. This is an extension of the argument for fencing the forests. As a common resource, they are ransacked. As private property, they may be managed and preserved. Is this extension of the idea of private property to genetic resources part of the price we will have to pay to live on a planet under global management? Or can we find other social mechanisms to do the same job?

HIGH-TECH EDEN

In June 1989 eight people will walk into a large greenhouse covering just over six hectares of the Arizona desert. They will seal the airlocks and stay there, all being well, for two years. The greenhouse is called 'Biosphere II' and it is to be the first completely closed biological system designed and built by humans. (Biosphere I is the Earth, but we did not build that ourselves.)

Inside, along with the biospherians, will be some 10,000 species of organisms and ten million litres of water. Walter Adey, one of the designers of Biosphere II, told *New Scientist* that it would have several separate ecosystems: 'a mini-ocean, an estuary, a freshwater marsh, a salt marsh . . . streams, a lagoon, a sandy beach'. There will be a farm, a piece of tropical rainforest and savannah grassland as well as 'trade winds' driven from desert to rainforest by the Sun's heat streaming through the greenhouse glass. The Sun's energy will be the only thing allowed either into or out of the biosphere. The oxygen given up by plants will be breathed by a zoo of animals, which will provide the carbon dioxide for plants to breathe. There will be a sterilizer for human waste and a purifier for drinking water. Air will be cleaned by percolating it through soil and hoping that the micro-biological inhabitants will do the job.

Nobody knows if the biospherians will be able to last the two years. Perhaps air pollution will make their environment intolerable; maybe some unsuspected breed of algae will take over and starve them out; maybe the social life will be unbearable. The point, of course, is to find out.

The project offers the chance to think about what a self-sustaining colony of people on the Moon or Mars would need in order to create an environment that does not rely on spaceships carrying supplies from Earth. But there must be a nagging feeling that one day we might need to do the same thing on Earth. Two Gaians, Dorion Sagan and Lynn Margulis from Boston University, offered this uncomfortable scenario to a conference in 1987:

> Widespread biosphere production will be mandated by pollution of the global commons. As the worldwide water supply diminishes, garbage bobs in the waves of the Arctic Ocean and the airspace over the Earth putrefies, biospheres begin to look more attractive. They become oases. Originally a luxury, biosphere-building eventually becomes obligatory. Survival inside a biosphere becomes more probable than outside.

Sagan and Margulis wonder whether this is not a natural development. We have parcelled up between us the land, which was once commonly owned, why not parcel up the air as well? 'As a sort of 3-D private property, biospheres will be required to ensure clean air, fresh water and edible food.' As biologists, they say that this 'fractionation' is what evolution is about. It is what allowed the development of cell structures that created higher life forms. 'It is bewitching,' they say, 'that biosphere production — ostensibly such a technological, human process — mirrors previous developments in evolutionary history, such as the formation of quietly functional, dormant, walled-off structures by cells.' Single cells with walls got together to create multicellular organisms. Maybe the next step is 'multiorganismic ecosystems'. Future biospheres might, if our planet's environment gets out of hand, turn into Gaian arks, sealed containers holding the essence of our planet's ecosystems and setting off into space to find a new world, like a seed blown through a forest.

This is fun, if fanciful. But maybe we would do best sticking with our present planet. The idea of biospheres provides an equally interesting vision of our future on Earth. The scale of human influence on the Earth today is forcing us to consider our impact on the planet's basic life-support systems. We cannot, as some romantics might wish, go back to the days before we had that impact. For good or ill, we must confront our power over the planet and learn how to manage it. We must, in short, begin to treat Biosphere I as the experimenters in the Arizona desert are treating Biosphere II. We are, to coin a phrase, all biospherians now.

Is this vision, in which nature is no longer free, a hellish one? Lovelock sometimes thinks so. In his first book on Gaia, he pondered the prospect of our so disabling Gaia, so disrupting the natural systems that sustain life on Earth, that 'we would wake up one day to find that we had a lifelong job of planetary maintenance engineer'. We could so overrun our planet, he said, that we eventually face 'the final choice of permanent enslavement on the prison hulk of spaceship Earth, or gigadeath to enable the survivors to restore a Gaian world'. Others, more pleasantly, see the new world as a garden: something tended by humans, but operating according to the laws of nature. Gardening sounds a better job than planetary maintenance engineer.

Lovelock hopes for an intellectual harmony with Gaia. 'To what extent is our collective intelligence a part of Gaia?' he wonders. 'Do we as a species constitute a Gaian nervous system and a brain which can consciously anticipate environmental changes? Whether we like it or not, we are already beginning to function in this way.' As science, this may be wild. But as metaphor, it is illuminating.

> The evolution of *Homo sapiens*, with his technological inventiveness and his increasingly subtle communications network, has vastly increased Gaia's range of perception. She is now, through us, awake and aware of herself . . . It may be that the destiny of mankind is to become tamed, so that the fierce, destructive, and greedy forces of tribalism and nationalism are fused into a compulsive urge to belong to the commonwealth of all creatures which constitutes Gaia.

This is the optimistic vision I prefer. A high-tech Eden in which we took the apple and lived to tell the tale.

GLOSSARY

Acid rain: Rain made acid by gaseous air pollutants, notably sulphur dioxide and nitrogen oxides.

Albedo: A measure of the reflectivity of a surface.

Biological pump: The method by which living organisms at the surface of the oceans draw carbon dioxide out of the atmosphere and, as they fall, deposit it on the ocean bottom. The pump has the effect of controlling the temperature of the atmosphere.

Blooms: Blossom, in this case the explosive growth of algae in the ocean when there is a surfeit of nutrients.

CFCs: Chlorofluorocarbons, the man-made chemical largely responsible for the recent thinning of the ozone layer.

Continental shelf: The expanses of shallow ocean floor that are geologically part of the continental land masses.

El Niño: The 'little boy'. The term for the periodic arrival of warm waters in the eastern Pacific. It is now known to be linked to the Southern Oscillation of atmospheric pressure.

ENSO: *El Niño*/Southern Oscillation, a term commonly used to describe the phenomenon of the two linked events.

Evapotranspiration: The combination of evaporation and transpiration by which rainwater is swiftly recycled from forest trees back into the air.

Fossil fuels: Coal, oil, gas and lignite. Fossilized vegetation which was deposited in swamps millions of years ago and is now being dug up for fuel. When burned, it releases carbon dioxide, adding to the greenhouse effect.

Free radicals: Chemicals such as hydroxyl and chlorine monoxide which rapidly oxidize other chemicals. They act as cleansers of pollution in the atmosphere.

Gaia: The idea, developed by Jim Lovelock and others, that the Earth is somehow 'alive' and that living organisms collectively control their own environment on the planet.

Greenhouse effect: The warming of the Earth caused by 'greenhouse gases' such as carbon dioxide and methane, which allow the Sun's radiation to reach the Earth but trap infra-red radiation reflected back from the planet's surface. The effect is a permanent feature of the planet, but is being enhanced by extra emissions of greenhouse gases caused by human activities.

Gulf Stream: Tropical ocean current that keeps Europe warm, especially in winter. It appears to have been 'turned off' during ice ages.

Ice ages: Recurrent spells of cold climate round the globe, which have appeared roughly once every 100,000 years for at least the past million years.

IGBP: International Geosphere Biosphere Programme, a major programme of research into global change scheduled for the 1990s.

Interglacial: The period between ice ages. The word 'super-interglacial' has been coined to describe the extra-warm, interglacial era on which the world appears about to embark.

Milankovitch wobbles: Cyclic oscillations in the orbit of the Earth and its relation to the Sun which may trigger ice ages. Named after the man who developed theories about their importance, Milutin Milankovitch.

NASA: National Aeronautics and Space Administration, the US's space agency.

Ozone layer: The ozone within the stratosphere which protects the Earth from ultraviolet radiation from the Sun.

Photosynthesis: the process by which plants synthesize organic material from carbon dioxide and water using energy from sunlight.

Glossary

Plankton: the mass of small organisms which float in the surface layers of the oceans. Phytoplankton are plant plankton. Algae are the largest sub-group of phytoplankton.

Plate tectonics: The notion that the Earth's surface is made up of a series of mobile plates. Their movement, which creates the current configuration of continents, is often known as 'continental drift'.

Polar vortex: The enclosed circulation of cold air which forms over the Antarctic and, in a modified form, the Arctic, each winter.

Positive feedback: The mechanism by which a change creates other changes which accentuate the original change. Thus if greenhouse warming causes plants or the ocean to release carbon dioxide, this will accentuate the greenhouse warming.

ppm: Parts per million. Likewise ppb is parts per billion.

Sahel: A zone of Africa just south of the Sahara desert, stretching from Mauritania to Sudan, which is especially prone to drought.

Shifting cultivators: Forest dwellers who clear farm land for a few years before moving on, thus allowing the original land to renew its fertility. Sometimes known as 'slashers and burners' after their methods of clearing forests.

Southern Oscillation: The characteristic shift in atmospheric pressures across the Pacific Ocean that coincides with *El Niño*. Together, the two are often called ENSO.

Strangelove ocean: A term adopted by some scientists to describe a lifeless ocean after, for instance, a nuclear disaster or the impact of a meteorite.

Stratosphere: Layer of the atmosphere, above 10–15 kilometres up, within which temperatures rise with altitude and the protective shield of ozone forms.

Stromatolites: Sedimentary rocks made up of fossilized algae.

Tropopause: The boundary between the troposphere and the stratosphere.

Troposphere: The bottom 10–15 kilometres of the atmosphere, where our weather occurs.

Tundra: Strip of land across northern continents which separates the ice caps from the most northern extent of the boreal forests. Characterized by permanently frozen subsoil.

Ultraviolet radiation: Radiation with wavelengths shorter than light but longer than X-rays. Harmful to living organisms, which are protected on Earth by the ozone layer.

UNEP: United Nations Environment Programme.

Waldsterben: German name for the strange sickness of trees which first afflicted central Europe and parts of North America in the early 1980s.

WMO: World Meteorological Organization, an agency of the United Nations.

BIBLIOGRAPHY

Few books have covered the range of issues I have attempted to tackle here. One such is *Sustainable Development of the Biosphere*, edited by Clark and Munn from the International Institute for Applied Systems Analysis, an independent and prestigious 'think tank' based in Laxenburg, Austria, and published in 1986 by Cambridge University Press. It is a pioneering effort. NASA, which has enviable supplies of money, scientists and satellites for viewing the world from space, has found itself in a pivotal position to investigate many of the issues of global change. In January 1988, it published *Earth System Science: A Closer View*, a review of the science that may help us to chart a course into the next century and beyond. More detail is contained in NASA's report *From Pattern to Process*: *The Strategy of the Earth Observing System*.

In 1986, *New Scientist* published with Blackwell a collection of articles on climate and atmospheric change which had appeared in the magazine in the previous decade. It was called *The Breathing Planet*. The magazine continues to report regularly on most of the topics I have written about here. Journals that regularly cover the field are headed by *Nature*, *Science* and Stephen Schneider's *Climatic Change*.

INTRODUCTION:

Hansen's predictions for changes in global climate, the science behind the buzz he created at the Senate hearings in

215

June 1988, appeared in the *Journal of Geophysical Research* (vol. 93, p. 9341-6, 1988). The proceedings of the conference on 'The Changing Atmosphere', held in Toronto in June 1988, were set for publication by the World Meteorological Organization. An edited version of McElroy's paper to that conference appeared in *New Scientist* on 28 July 1988.

I THROUGH THE OZONE HOLE

The first popular book on the ozone hole, its science and implications, is *The Hole in the Sky* by John Gribbin (Corgi, 1988). Otherwise, much of the science is still confined to journals and science magazines. *Nature* and *Science* are the essential journals. The details of the debates are moving too fast for it to be worth my recommending many particular papers or articles. Specialist science writers worth following are John Gribbin in *New Scientist*, Richard Kerr in *Science* and Pamela Zurer in *Chemical and Engineering News*. Also, NASA publishes an 'Upper Atmospheric Programs Bulletin'.

The key papers are Farman's revelation about the ozone hole (*Nature*, vol. 315, p. 207–10, 1985) and the seminal paper on how CFCs might destroy ozone by Rowland and Molina (*Nature*, vol. 249, p. 810–12, 1974). Robin Russell Jones published a good review of the cancer risks from ozone loss in *The Lancet*, 22 August 1987.

2 HOW THINGS BEGAN

Jim Lovelock, the inventor of Gaia, is a persuasive and eloquent writer. Early expositions include a paper written with Lynn Margulis for *Tellus* (vol. 26, p. 1, 1974) and another in *New Scientist* (6 February 1975). A fascinating account of his life's work appeared, again in *New Scientist*, on 6 September 1979, under the title 'The Independent Practice of Science'. His first Gaian book, *Gaia, A New Look at Life on Earth*, first published in 1979 by Oxford University Press, is a delight. The best current exposition of the anti-Gaian views of Walker, Kasting and company, including an overview of the evolution of Mars and Venus, appeared in *Scientific American*, February 1988. Taking the middle ground is Stephen Schneider, the loquacious climate modeller, who, with a journalist, Randi Londer, wrote the 560-page *The Coevolution of Climate and Life*, published in 1984 by Sierra Club Books, San Francisco.

Sagan and Mullen first mentioned the feint early-Sun paradox in *Science* (vol. 177, p. 52, 1972). The debate about mass extinctions continues in the journals, notably *Science*. The paper by Luis and Walter Alvarez on an 'extraterrestrial cause' for the extinction of the dinosaurs appeared in *Science* (vol. 208, p. 1095–108, 1980).

Most of the topics in this chapter were debated at length at the conference on Gaia, organized by Schneider and held under the auspices of the American Geophysical Union in March 1988. The AGU was expected to publish the proceedings of that conference in 1989.

3 SHIFTING SANDS

There is a lot of well-meaning rubbish written about the plight of Africa and the spread of its deserts. Partly, this seems to be because environmentalists, economists and climatologists seem uninterested in talking to each other. Two books that break down the barriers are Paul Harrison's *The Greening of Africa*, published in 1987 by Paladin for the International Institute for Environment and Development, and *Drought and Hunger in Africa*, edited by Michael Glantz, a climatologist, and published by Cambridge University Press. This latter book includes the study by Horowitz and Little on African pastoralism. Glantz's article in *Scientific American* in June 1987 on 'Drought in Africa' is also excellent.

Debora MacKenzie's articles on Ethiopia in *New Scientist* were published on 24 September and 1 October 1987. I also like her look at East African herders ('A Hoof-up for Africa's Livestock') in *New Scientist* on 25 June 1987. Rattan Lal's study on 'Managing the Soils of Sub-Saharan Africa' appeared in *Science* in 1987 (vol. 236, p. 1069–76). Derek Winstanley's unheeded warning that the Sahel was embarking on several decades of drought first appeared in *Nature* in 1973 (vol. 245, p. 190–5).

4 LIFE AND DEATH OF THE RAINFORESTS

Deforestation is another area prone to simple-minded warnings of doom. Emotive but fascinating, especially on the plight of the forests' inhabitants, is *In The Rainforest* by Catherine Caufield (Heinemann, 1985). I quote at length the investigation of the recent history of West African forests by Vivien Gornitz, which appeared in *Climatic Change* (vol. 7, p. 285–325, 1985). Another attempt at cool-headedness is the review by Sedjo and Clawson in *The Resourceful Earth*, edited by Simon and Kahn (see notes on Chapter 12). *Ambio*, a journal of environmental sciences published by the Swedish Academy of Sciences, ran a good study of the loss of trees in the south-eastern Amazon basin (vol. 17, p. 49–55, 1988). The fascinating experiment by Pedro Sanchez in farming the soils of the Amazon basin appeared in *Science* (vol. 216, p. 821–7, 1982).

The father of modern thought on how forests might change climate was Jule Charney with his paper in the *Quarterly Journal of the Royal Meteorological Society* (vol. 101, p. 193, 1975). The debate was carried forward by Sagan and others in *Science* (vol. 206, p. 1363–8, 1979) and by Gornitz (see above). Salati's pioneering work on the Amazon 'water machine', 'Amazon Basin: A System in Equilibrium', appeared in *Science* (vol. 225, p. 129–38, 1984), and Mintz and others modelled the effect on world climates of chopping down all the forests also in *Science* (vol. 215, p. 1498–501, 1982).

5 BUGS ON CLOUD NINE

Schnell's work on bacteria that cause clouds has languished in relative obscurity. Only Gaians have taken much interest. His paper on hailstorms over Kenyan tea plantations ap eared in *Tellus* (vol. 34, p. 92–5, 1982).

Lovelock's work on planktonic sulphur and clouds, on the other hand, has brought Gaia some scientific respectability. The important paper, written by Lovelock, Andreae, Charlson and Warren, appeared in *Nature* (vol. 326, p. 655–61, 1987). Charlson firmed up some of the links in the same journal (vol. 329, p. 319–21, 1987) and Richard Monastersky wrote a good review of the sulphur story in *Science News* on 5 December 1987.

6 TURNING UP THE HEAT

Broecker's invective is from an angry article, entitled 'Unpleasant Surprises in the Greenhouse?' and published in *Nature* in 1987 (vol. 328, p. 123–6). There are several texts on model predictions of the 'surprise-free' greenhouse. Perhaps the best, edited by Bolin and others, called *The Greenhouse Effect, Climatic Change and Ecosystems*, is a product of the Scientific Committee on Problems of the Environment (SCOPE), a committee of the International Council of Scientific Unions and was published by John Wiley in 1986. For weight, try the four 'state-of-the-art' volumes from the Carbon Dioxide Research Division of the US government's Department of Energy, published in 1985.

As this book went to press, the most up-to-date review of the greenhouse theory itself came from Veerhabadrhan Ramanathan in *Science* (vol. 240, p. 293–9, 1988). One of the best and most accessible reviews of the consequences of the greenhouse for climate is still Roger Revelle's 'Carbon Dioxide and World Climate' in *Scientific American*, August 1982. Manabe and Wetherald made an important contribution in their report on modelling soil wetness in *Science* (vol. 232, p. 626–8, 1986). Graeme Pearman's pioneering study of the likely impact of greenhouse warming on Australian life was set for publication by the Australian government's research agency, the CSIRO, late in 1988. Pittock's look at extreme events is published by the Australian Academy of Sciences in the proceedings of a 1988 conference on global change. Some of his calculations derive from Wigley (*Nature*, vol. 316, p. 106–7, 1985). William Clark of the IIASA published an important study of 'Scales of Climatic Impacts' for the journal *Climatic Change* (vol. 7, p. 5–27, 1985).

Alayne Street published his study of past lake levels across Africa in *Nature* (vol. 261, p. 385–90, 1976).

7 STRANGE CASE OF THE MISSING CARBON

The row about the destruction of forests and the carbon cycle rumbled on for a decade in the journals. Some early highlights include Woodwell's assertions in *Science* (vol. 199, p. 141, 1978 and vol. 222, p. 1081–6, 1983) and Broecker's initial response, again in *Science* (vol. 206, p. 409–18, 1979). Myers' controversial study of deforestation for the US National Research Council, *Conversion of Tropical Moist Forests*, was published by the National Academy of Sciences in 1980. Myers, Woodwell and others retreated from their earlier stance in a paper in *Nature* (vol. 316, p. 617–20, 1985). Hall and Detwiler published their assessment in *Science* (vol. 239, p. 42–7, 1988).

The UN Environment Programme's generally useful report on 'The Greenhouse Gases' (part of its GEMS Environment Library series) discusses how 'plants will grow bigger'. Woodwell is back with warnings of the implications of the destruction of trees due to global warming in the excellent winter 1986/87 issue of the magazine *Oceanus* (from the Woods Hole Oceanographic Institution) devoted to changing climate.

D'Arrigo's prediction of boom rather than bust for boreal forests appears in *Nature* (vol. 329, p. 321–3, 1987) and followed a less optimistic study by Gammon, Keeling and others in the same journal (vol. 319, p. 195–9, 1986).

8 THE SHAPE OF THINGS TO COME?

The immediate consequences of the 1982–83 *El Niño* were reviewed in *Science* at the end of 1983 (vol. 222, p. 1189–1210). Work on the subsequent evolution of Darwin's finches was summarized in *Nature* (vol. 327, p. 461, 1987). Cane, who compiled the *Science* summary of the oceanographic consequences of the 1983 *El Niño*, successfully predicted the 1986–87 event. A review of that prediction, made with Barnett and others, appeared in *Science* (vol. 241, p. 192–6, 1988), complementing a new review of the science of *El Niño* as a 'natural oscillator' by Graham and White, published in the same journal (vol. 240, p. 1293–302, 1988).

Barnett published his evidence linking *El Niño* with snow cover on land and monsoons, again in *Science*, in late 1987 (vol. 239, p. 504–7).

9 THE CAUSES OF ICE AGES

There are many summaries of Milankovitch's ideas and their interpretation by physicists in the greenhouse age. One of the best is by John Gribbin in his book *Future Weather* (Penguin, 1982). The new work on evidence of sudden change derived from the Vostok ice core data has mostly appeared in *Nature* (see especially vol. 329, p. 403–18, 1987). Broecker wrote about changes in deep ocean circulation during ice ages in 1987 (vol. 315, p. 21–6) and Shackleton and Duplessy followed up later that year (vol. 316, p. 500–6). Broecker reiterated his fears that switches in ocean circulation could cause 'unpleasant surprises in the greenhouse' in *Nature* in 1987 (vol. 328, p. 123–6).

Polynyas in the Southern Ocean are described in *Scientific American* (June 1988) by Gordon and Comiso. Broecker and colleagues reported the current freshening of the far north Atlantic in *Science* (vol. 222, p. 1237–9, 1983). Crowley and North suggested that climatic flips, based perhaps on changes in deep-ocean circulation, may not require extra-terrestrial triggers in an important paper, 'Abrupt Climatic Change and Extinction Events in Earth History', in *Science* (vol. 240, p. 996–1002, 1988). The most concise description of the biological pump and how it might trigger ice ages is offered by Michael McElroy in IIASA's estimable report, mentioned earlier, *Sustainable Development of the Biosphere*. McCarthy describes fluxes of life-giving chemicals in the oceans in the special issue of *Oceanus* devoted to climatic change, mentioned above. Finally, Martin and Fitzwater brought iron into the debate in a paper in *Nature* (vol. 331, p. 341–3, 1988).

10 GREENHOUSE COCKTAIL

The rise in concentrations of methane in the atmosphere is increasingly well documented, even if the sources and sinks are uncertain. Valuable reviews include Dieter Ehhalt's in the magazine *Environment* in December 1985; a series of articles on methane in *Science* (vol. 318, p. 245–57, 1985) and a paper on methane data from the Vostok ice core in *Nature* (vol. 333, p. 655–7, 1988). The study on termites turned up in *Science* (vol. 218, p. 563–5, 1982).

Rasmussen and Khalil have been foremost in accumulating data on trace gases in the atmosphere. They reviewed the field for *Science* in 1986 (vol. 232, p. 1623–4) and examined the links between carbon monoxide and hydroxyl in *Nature* in 1988 (vol. 332, p. 242–5). Penkett reviewed the increase in tropospheric ozone in *Nature* in 1988 (vol. 332, p. 204–5).

11 BEFORE THE FLOOD

The expansion of sea water through warming of the water appears to have been in progress for some time. The effects are small but fairly predictable, as shown by Wigley and Raper (*Nature*, vol. 330, p. 127–31, 1987). Much less predictable is when and whether the great ice sheets will begin to melt. Henderson-Sellers and McGuffie surveyed the scene for *New Scientist* (12 June 1986), which also revealed evidence that there were 'green hills' at the South Pole two million years ago (3 July 1986). Oerlemans and van der Veen in *Ice Sheets and Climate* (Reidel, 1984) and a report by the US Department of Energy on 'Glaciers, Ice Sheets and Sea Level: Effect of a Carbon Dioxide-Induced Climatic Change' both took a sanguine view of the return of the green hills. The opposite view is put most forcefully by Mercer in *Nature* (vol. 271, p. 321–5, 1978).

12 A QUESTION OF NUMBERS

The Limits To Growth by Meadows appeared in 1972 under the imprint of Universe Books. *Science* reported its launch in vol. 175, p. 1088–92, 1972. Ehrlich's *The Population Bomb* was published by Ballantine in 1968. Caldwell delivered the quoted rebuke for both books in an article called 'Man and his Futures', published in *Search*, the journal of the Australian and New Zealand Association for the

Advancement of Science (ANZAAS) in February–March 1985. The *Global 2000 Report to the President* was published by the US government in 1980. Julian Simon's rabidly subversive tome, *The Ultimate Resource*, appeared from Princeton University Press in 1981. He pursued the theme in another book, *The Resourceful Earth*, edited with Herman Kahn and published by Blackwell in 1984. Much of this chapter is based on my own research for an article for *New Scientist* ('In Defence of Population Growth', 9 August 1984). I returned to the theme in 'Mexico, the City Unlimited' (18 October 1984) and 'Welcome to the Global Old Folks' Home' (9 July 1987).

Interesting debunking of fears that natural resources will run out appeared in *Technology Review* ('How Critical are Critical Materials?' August–September 1985) and in Zucker's 'Infinite Resources: The Ultimate Strategy' in *Science* (vol. 223, p. 456–62, 1984).

13 TURNING DOWN THE HEAT

'The Management of Sea-Level Rise' by storing water on land is the brainchild of Newman and Fairbridge (*Nature*, vol. 320, p. 319–21, 1986). Steinberg's assessment of 'decarbonization' at power stations is published as 'A Systems Study for the Removal, Recovery and Disposal of Carbon Dioxide from Fossil Fuel Power Plants in the US' by the US Department of Energy in 1986. Marland proposes planting trees for a cooler world in another DOE report, 'The Prospects of Solving the Carbon Dioxide Problem Through Global Reforestation', published in 1988. Steinberg's review of save-it strategies emerges from the DOE as 'Effects of Energy Technology on Global Carbon Dioxide Emissions'. Several such strategies, including Green's, were discussed at a session of the annual meeting of the American Association for the Advancement of Science (AAAS) in 1988, which also included papers by Steinberg and Marland.

The IIASA's grand plan for a Novel Integrated Energy System is reviewed in its book, *Sustainable Development of the Biosphere*. Irving Mintzer's important synthesis of economic and climatic models was published as 'A Matter of

Degrees: The Potential for Controlling the Greenhouse Effect' by the World Resources Institute in 1987. He also presented a paper on the idea to the 'Changing Atmosphere' conference in Toronto in June 1988. Laurmann's article on 'setting the priorities' and predicting surprises in global warming appeared in *Climatic Change* (vol. 7, p. 261–5, 1985). The conclusions of the US National Research Council's workshop on atmospheric change were published by the National Academy Press in 1987.

POSTSCRIPT: ALL ABOARD THE GAIAN ARK

Raven's review of 'The Global Ecosystem in Crisis', given to the AAAS annual conference in 1987, was published later that year as an occasional paper by the MacArthur Foundation in Chicago. Mooney's excellent review of 'The Law of the Seed', from which I quote, appeared as a special double issue of *Development Dialogue*, a journal published by the Dag Hammarskjöld Foundation in Uppsala, Sweden.

Gaian biospheres are the product of the fertile minds of Margulis and Sagan, as presented to a small conference on Gaia held at the Wadebridge Ecological Centre in Lovelock's home county of Cornwall in late 1987.

INDEX

acid rain, 49–50, 93–4, 123, 157, 161–2, 164–5, 188, 192, 211

Africa, 5, 10, 54–5, 57–76, 80–2, 86–9, 103–8, 120, 125–6, 129–30, 132–3, 150–1, 169, 175, 184–6, 188, 190–1, 201–2, 213

algae, 26–7, 43–4, 89–93, 153–6, 213

Alvarez, Walter, 46–8, 51, 217

Amazon rainforest, 5, 9, 11, 75–85, 115, 124, 129, 145, 158, 204–5

Anderson, Jim, 13, 19, 21, 31, 162–3

Andreae, Meinrat, 90, 218

Antarctica, ice cores, 135–6, 147, 151, 158;
ice sheets, 5, 170;
ozone hole, 5, 9, 11–16, 18–24, 26–7, 31–3;
warming predictions, 100, 102, 199, 201

Antarctic Ocean, 139–40, 144, 149–50

Aral Sea, 105–6, 190–1

Arctic, atmosphere, 166;

ice cap, 10, 100, 142, 153, 168, 201;
ozone over, 29–31;
rocks beneath, 158;
trees in, 122, 124

Arctic Ocean, life in, 144, 149

Arrhenuis, Svante, 97

Atlantic, North, 139–42, 147–9, 152–3

Australia, 5, 54, 119, 124, 159, 169, 175;
and ENSO, 125, 129–30, 133;
and greenhouse warming, 104, 108–12;
and ozone hole, 13, 23–4, 33

Bangladesh, 11, 68–9, 106, 130, 169, 194

Barnett, Tim, 132–3, 220–1

Bermuda Triangle, 159

biological pump, 42, 139, 143–7, 150–3, 211

biospheres, 207–8

Bolin, Bert, 37, 156, 219

Brazil, 69, 75–81, 184, 204;
see also Amazon rainforest

Broecker, Wally, 95, 115, 118,

225